dear friends,

This year, Stampin' Up!® celebrates a significant milestone—our 15-year a[...]
involved during the past decade and a half with people who love to create through the art of
rubber stamping has been a rewarding, enjoyable experience—both professionally and personally.

Of course, much has happened in 15 years. Back then, my family consisted of my husband, our
five daughters, and me. Obviously, the Gardner family has grown! And so has the Stampin' Up!
family. From the beginning, however, Stampin' Up! has been committed to providing rubber
stampers and scrapbookers with the tools and ideas they need to express their feelings, share
their creativity, and preserve memories.

You'll certainly see that commitment in every page of our new *2003–2004 Idea Book & Catalog*.
Here you'll find hundreds of new stamp sets and accessories that make it both fun and easy to
decorate your home and create handmade cards, gifts, craft projects, and scrapbook pages.
You'll also love the hundreds of inspiring, full-color samples. And if you're interested in scrapbooking, you'll enjoy the *Stampin' Memories® Idea Book & Catalog*, which includes many more
page layouts and our complete line of Stampin' Memories products.

For 15 years, Stampin' Up! has dedicated itself to providing people with exactly what they
need to express their creativity. I am confident this Idea Book & Catalog will continue that
time-honored tradition and inspire you to create many wonderful works from the heart.

Shelli

Shelli Gardner
Cofounder and CEO

left to right: Grandson Sam, son-in-law Sean, grandaughter Sidney, Sara, grandson Seth, Shalae, Shelli, Sterling, grandson Cameron, Sage, Shanna, grandaughter Olivia, son-in-law Nate, grandson Zach, Megan, and grandson Tanner

1

contents

share what you love

love what you do

make a difference

enjoy creativity

our products

Stampin' Up! is proud to present an Idea Book & Catalog full of our exclusive, innovative stamping and crafting products. This year, you'll find more than 125 fabulous new stamp sets and wheels, many in the wonderful styles you've come to love from Stampin' Up!, along with several exciting new styles. With stamps ranging from whimsical and realistic to vintage and classic, you are sure to find the perfect stamps to suit your personal style, whether you are making a card, creating a scrapbook page, or decorating a room in your home. And as always, our stamp sets are carefully planned with a selection of images, greetings, backgrounds, and borders to provide you the greatest versatility.

In addition to our wonderful stamps sets, Stampin' Up! carries an amazing array of accessories to perfectly embellish your artwork. All of our basic accessories, including card stock, markers, ink pads and cartridges, and Stampin' Pastels®, come in Stampin' Up!'s exclusive 48-color palette, making it easy to create beautiful projects with our color-coordinated products. Stampin' Up! also features great embellishments to add the final touch that turns a simple project into an eye-catching masterpiece! This year, joining long-time favorites such as eyelets, ribbon, hemp, and Wire Works are several great new accessories: eyelets in eight new shapes, Fancy Fibers, Metal Edge Tags, tag sheets in 12 x 12, Premo Sculpey™ clay, and exclusive die-cut boxes. You'll also want to see the exciting additions to our ever-popular Classy Brass® templates.

With our incredible selection of products, Stampin' Up! is committed to your creativity and artistic expression. You can count on our superior products for all your works of heart!

box it

Stampin' Up!'s new die-cut boxes are available in many sizes, shapes, and colors. Easy to fold and assemble, our boxes allow you to create customized packaging.

stampin' memories®

Stampin' Up! is pleased to provide a complete line of scrapbooking products to help you preserve your precious family memories. From our versatile Designer Series paper and vellum to our quick and easy Simply Scrappin'® kits, Stampin' Up!'s exclusive products feature beautiful artwork unavailable anywhere else. Our wide range of stamps and accessories can help you create a variety of moods in your scrapbooks, whether you're making a family heritage book full of old-time photos and memorabilia, recording your child's growth and activities, or preserving travel memories. Scrapbooking has never been so fun or so easy!

In addition to the great stamp sets and scrapbooking samples in this *2003–2004 Idea Book & Catalog*, our biannual *Stampin' Memories Idea Book & Catalog* offers a full range of scrapbook-specific stamps—phrases, frames, and corners—as well as exclusive albums and accessories. Also look to Stampin' Up! for all of your basic scrapbooking needs, such as archival-quality adhesives, markers, and page protectors. Contact your demonstrator today to see a copy of the current *Stampin' Memories Idea Book & Catalog*.

write it

Stampin' Up!'s *Write Me a Memory*™ Journaling Fonts CD makes journaling easier than ever! Just select 1 of the 10 handwritten fonts, and write your story.

two-step stampin'®

Creating multicolored art is quick and easy with Two-Step Stampin'—it's just two steps to colorful, vibrant images! First, stamp the base image with a light color. Then use a darker color to stamp the corresponding detail image. By doing the two-step, you can create the background and the detail of any image with two or three separate stamps, as shown on the flower and leaves below.

This timesaving technique adds color to your images without requiring markers, pencils, or chalks. Use coordinating or contrasting color for different effects—you choose. You'll find Two-Step Stampin' sets throughout the catalog; just look for the Two-Step Stampin' Logo (shown above).

color it

You'll love the results you can achieve with Two-Step Stampin' sets. Some sets are designed for layering, while others include adjoining images. Either way, you can create colorful projects in no time!

use these stamps . . .

to create this . . .

definitely decorative®

Rubber stamping isn't just for cards and scrapbook pages—Stampin' Up!'s line of Definitely Decorative stamps is specially designed for people who want to create customized home décor. Each Definitely Decorative stamp set contains several coordinating stamps you can use to add a personal touch to walls, lampshades, frames, furniture, and more! The images are bold and oversized, so you can cover wall space or interiors quickly.

Whether you want to create a room with a look that's playful, rustic, delicate, or elegant, you'll find a Definitely Decorative set that's just right for you—at a fraction of the cost of conventional redecorating!

Look for Definitely Decorative stamp sets shown in color throughout the catalog.

decorate it
Definitely Decorative stamp sets include large and bold images that are designed to quickly cover wall space, but they are also an excellent choice for any stamping project. Use them for cards, scrapbook pages, and gift wrap!

stampin' around®

With Stampin' Up!'s exclusive line of Stampin' Around wheels, you can create fun patterned backgrounds in seconds! Our Stampin' Around system provides nonstop stamping for borders, backgrounds, gift packaging, and more.

Available in more than 70 exclusive designs, many wheels coordinate with our terrific stamp sets—giving you more creative options than ever!

Stampin' Around ink cartridges and refills are available in Stampin' Up!'s 48 exclusive colors to ensure beautifully coordinated creations. Or use our uninked cartridges to create your own color combinations. Whatever combination you choose, our wheels will have you Stampin' Around in no time!

Look for Stampin' Around wheels throughout the catalog. For a complete listing, turn to pages 205–207.

wheel it

Remove the lid of the ink cartridge, then slide the cartridge directly against the wheel for continuous stamping. Our interchangeable cartridges allow you to change colors quickly and easily.

hostess rewards

Stampin' Up! hostesses open their homes and provide a warm environment for demonstrators to present fun and informative workshops. To reward our hostesses, Stampin' Up! offers free hostess-only stamp sets and additional free Stampin' Up! products based on the total net sales of the workshop!

And as if this weren't enough, Stampin' Up!'s hostesses are also eligible to receive a free Hostess Appreciation Set each quarter! This set is only available to hostesses—please contact your demonstrator for more information and to see the current Hostess Appreciation Set.

hostess benefits

Net Workshop Total	Hostess Sets			Hostess Awards
	Level 1 ABCDEF	Level 2 ABCD	Level 3 AB	Free Merchandise Totaling Up To:
$150.00 - $199.99	Choose 1	—	—	$15.00
$200.00 - $249.99	Choose 1	—	—	$20.00
$250.00 - $299.99	Choose 1	—	—	$25.00
$300.00 - $349.99	Choose 1 **or** Choose 1		—	$35.00
$350.00 - $399.99	Choose 1 **or** Choose 1		—	$40.00
$400.00 - $449.99	Choose 1 **or** Choose 1		—	$45.00
$450.00 - $499.99	Choose 1 **or** Choose 1		—	$50.00
$500.00 - $549.99	Choose 2	—	—	$60.00
	or			
	Choose 1	Choose 1	—	
	or			
	—	—	Choose 1	
$550.00 - $599.99	Choose 2	—	—	$65.00
	or			
	Choose 1	Choose 1	—	
	or			
	—	—	Choose 1	
$600.00 - $649.99	Choose 2	—	—	$75.00
	or			
	Choose 1	Choose 1	—	
	or			
	—	—	Choose 1	
$650.00 - $699.99	Choose 2	—	—	$85.00
	or			
	Choose 1	Choose 1	—	
	or			
	—	—	Choose 1	
$700.00 - $749.99	Choose 2	—	—	$95.00
	or			
	Choose 1	Choose 1	—	
	or			
	—	—	Choose 1	
$750.00 +	Choose 2	—	—	$100.00 plus 15% of amount over $750.00
	or			
	Choose 1	Choose 1	—	
	or			
	—	—	Choose 1	

No shipping and handling amounts are charged on hostess benefits.

Please see the Hostess Benefits Chart in the Canadian Supplement to the *2003–2004 Idea Book & Catalog* for Canadian Hostess Benefits.

Whether you want to learn about the latest stamping techniques, have a fun night with friends, or build your stamp collection, you'll love hosting a Stampin' Up! workshop! Contact your Stampin' Up! demonstrator today, or call 1-800-STAMP UP, to schedule your next workshop.

{ **1-800-STAMP UP**
www.stampinup.com }

may hope fill your heart

thanks

happy!
happy!
happy!

thanks

Level 1-A. Teeny Tinies
100014 (Set of 6)

HAPPY
FATHER'S
DAY

Level 1-B. Close to Nature
100016 (Set of 4)

many
thanks

for you

thinking
O F   Y O U

smile
smile
smile
smile
smile
smile

Level 1-C. Fresh Fillers
100196 (Set of 4)

Level 1-D. Simple Somethings
100012 (Set of 4)

Level 1-E. Mostly Flowers
100102 (Set of 4)

Level 1-F. Very Merry
100106 (Set of 4)

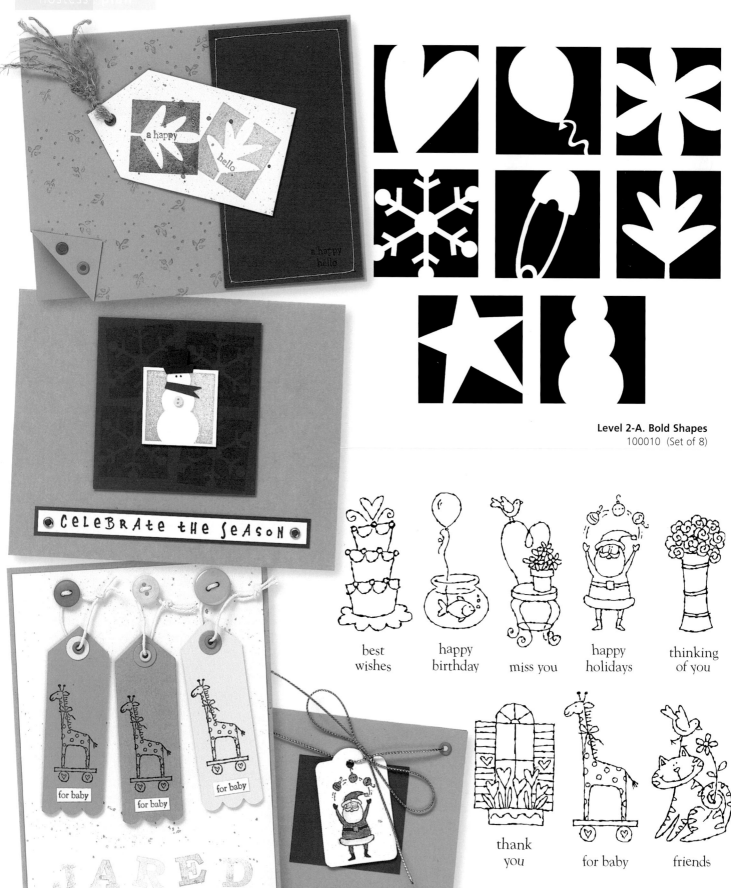

Level 2-A. Bold Shapes
100010 (Set of 8)

best wishes

happy birthday

miss you

happy holidays

thinking of you

thank you

for baby

friends

Level 2-B. Little Hellos
100198 (Set of 8)

Level 2-C. All Natural
100032 (Set of 6)

Level 2-D. Memory of the Heart
100200 (Set of 6)

Thank You

Thank You

Appreciation
is the
memory
of the heart.

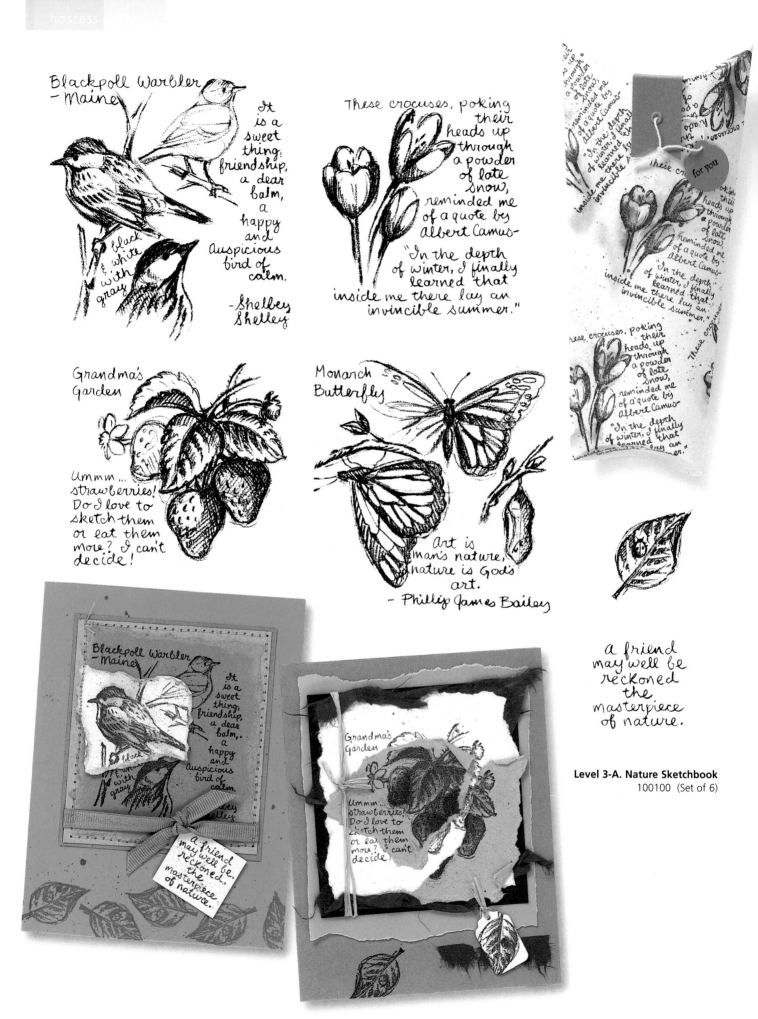

Blackpoll Warbler
- Maine

It is a sweet thing, friendship, a dear balm, a happy and auspicious bird of calm.

black & white with gray

-Shelbey Shelley

These crocuses, poking their heads up through a powder of late snow, reminded me of a quote by Albert Camus-

"In the depth of winter, I finally learned that inside me there lay an invincible summer."

Grandma's Garden

Ummm... strawberries! Do I love to sketch them or eat them more? I can't decide!

Monarch Butterfly

Art is man's nature, nature is God's art.
- Phillip James Bailey

a friend may well be reckoned the masterpiece of nature.

Level 3-A. Nature Sketchbook
100100 (Set of 6)

happy
everything!

celebrate you!

happily
ever after

happy new baby!

just because
i care...

thank you

thinking
of you

'tis the season

Level 3-B. Greetings Galore
100094 (Set of 8)

© 1990–2003 Stampin' Up!

FOREVER

Laura Jane Neeley
&
Chet Allan Ellis
have chosen
Saturday, the fourteenth of December
two thousand two
to be married in the
Manti Utah Temple

Please join us at
the celebration party
Friday, the thirteenth of December
from six-thirty until nine o'clock
in the evening

The Historic Southworth Hall
116 West Center Street
Provo, Utah

Forever Friends

To:

From:

Friends.

Hearts & Posies (Set of 6)
100791 can $34.95 | **US $21.95**

Love Ya!

Love Ya!

Love Ya! (Set of 8)
103079 can $28.95 | **US $17.95**

XO XO XO XO

102596 Stampin' Around® **Hugs & Kisses** can $9.50 | **US $5.95** (Wheel only. Handle and ink cartridges sold separately. See pages 204–211.)

LOVE

Happy Hearts (Set of 6)
100319 can $23.95 | **US $14.95**

kaTe had so much fun dressing
The parT of princess aT pre-
school. aFTer school she didn'T
wanT To change ouT of her
dress-ups. she wore Them all
day, and even asked To wear
Them To bed!

ocTober 2002

| LOVE YOU | YES | BE MINE | MISS YOU | HUG ME | KISS ME |

Sweetheart Candy II (Set of 6)
101586 can $15.95 | **US $9.95**

102254 Stampin' Around® **Love Swirls** can $9.50 | **US $5.95** (Wheel only. Handle and ink cartridges sold separately. See pages 204–211.)

Bear Hugs (Set of 8)
101257 can $26.95 | **us** **$16.95**

Be Mine (Set of 6)
100779 can $23.95 | **us** **$14.95**

POST CARD

CORRESPONDENCE · ADDRESS ONLY

Dear Lucy,
I arrived yesterday and the trip was lovely. Aunt Arlene is wonderful. She's showing me so many things and introducing me to some wonderful people. We send our love, Vera

PLACE STAMP HERE

TO:
Miss Lucy Mabey
Rt. 2, Box 12
Pleasant, Vermont

SNAIL MAIL

THANK YOU

PLACE STAMP HERE

TO:

FROM:

POST CARD

CORRESPONDENCE · ADDRESS ONLY

JUST A NOTE

SNAIL MAIL

PLACE STAMP HERE

THANK YOU

Vintage Postcard (Set of 9)
101000 can $36.95 | **US $22.95**

I Love You Truly

True Love (Set of 6)
100188 can $26.95 | **US $16.95**

HAPPY VALENTINE'S DAY

TO_____

FROM_____

Animal Valentines (Set of 6)
102380 can $29.95 | **US $18.95**

HOPPIN' YOU'LL BE MINE!

for you

HOPPIN' YOU'LL BE MINE!

Unforgettable...That's what you are!

HAPPY VALENTINE'S DAY !

hugs and kisses

BE MINE!

WISHING A PURRFECT FRIEND A PURRFECT DAY!

Have a Heart (Set of 7)
101999 can $31.95 | **US $19.95**

Kiss
me,
I'm
Irish!

Kiss me, I'm Irish! Kiss

Hearts & Clovers (Set of 6)
100382 can $23.95 | **US $14.95**

Wishing you
all the lovely
gifts of spring!

for you

Wishing you
all the lovely
gifts of spring!

PLANTS

Spring Gifts (Set of 6)
102507 can $31.95 | **US $19.95**

PLANTS

102291 Stampin' Around® **Spring Things** can $9.50 | **US $5.95** (Wheel only. Handle and ink cartridges sold separately. See pages 204–211.)

Happy Easter

Thinking of You

May each miracle
of Spring
be a sweet reminder
of God's
everlasting love.

Miracle of Spring (Set of 6)
100707 can $31.95 | **US $19.95**

EASTER
T R A D I T I O N

DYING EASTER
EGGS AT GRANDMA'S
HOUSE IS A FAVORITE
EASTER TRADITION.
MARCH 29, 2003

Eggcitement (Set of 7)
100245 can $28.95 | **US $17.95**

100352 Stampin' Around® **Spring** can $9.50 | **US $5.95** (Wheel only. Handle and ink cartridges sold separately. See pages 204–211.)

May the support of family and friends bring you comfort, and may loving memories heal your heart.

What the heart has once owned and had, it shall never lose.

—Henry Ward Beecher

With Sympathy

Loving Memories (Set of 4)
100414 can $28.95 | **US $17.95**

Hoping your day is filled with happiness!

Spring is nature's way of saying~ "Let's party"!

Spring Party (Set of 6)
102601 can $34.95 | **US $21.95**

102005 Stampin' Around® **Joy of Spring** can $9.50 | **US $5.95** (Wheel only. Handle and ink cartridges sold separately. See pages 204–211.)

Easter Blessings

I am the resurrection, and the life: he that believeth in me, though he were dead, yet shall he live...

John 11:25

Wishing you and those you love renewed faith and hope in Christ.

Renewed Faith (Set of 4)
100317 can $28.95 | **US** $17.95

Happy Easter

Wishing you all the wonderful gifts of spring.

hand-stamped by

The Gifts of Spring (Set of 6)
102813 can $34.95 | **US** $21.95

NICE CATCH

It was late in the afternoon and the guys told me the fish wouldn't be biting. They were surprised when I made the catch of the day. In fact, it turned out to be the biggest catch of the whole trip! August 2002

BeST FISHeS

Definitely Decorative® **Tropical Fish** (Set of 7)
103324 can $52.95 | **US $32.95**

Our Little TADPOLE LEARNS TO SWIM

The first swimming lesson for Judy is a fun one! alThough she is only 3 years old, she is eager To Learn and Follow her Teacher. our LiTTLe Tadpole is growing up.

hang in there

Definitely Decorative® **Leapfrogs** (Set of 6)
100861   Can $45.95 I **US $28.95**

Fly Fishing (Set of 6)
101217 can $34.95 | **US $21.95**

SKI LAKE MEAD

LAKE
MEAD

SUMMER
1994

Stipple Shells (Set of 6)
101580 can $23.95 | **US $14.95**

many
thanks

103094 Stampin' Around® **By the Sea** can $9.50 | **US $5.95** (Wheel only. Handle and ink cartridges sold separately. See pages 204–211.)

the best place to be is...

TOGETHER

Chet, my family, and I took a day trip to Little Cottonwood Canyon and hiked about a mile to Cecret Lake. The scenery was absolutely breathtaking.

spring
2003

you are invited to a

Birthday Campout

date: June 1, 2003

time: 5:30 pm

place: the backyard

for: Adam Spencer

RSVP · 654·6927

Roughing It (Set of 17)
101395 can $47.95 | **US $29.95**

Stars & Swirls (Set of 4)
100851 can $18.95 | **us $11.95**

I Love Canada (Set of 6)
102435 can $29.95 | **us $18.95**

101773 Stampin' Around® **Star-Spangled** can $9.50 | **us $5.95** (Wheel only. Handle and ink cartridges sold separately. See pages 204–211.)

God
bless
America!

Wishing you a
star-spangled
kind of day!

a happy
hello

Star-Spangled Day (Set of 7)
102830 can $31.95 | **US $19.95**

HAPPY BIRTHDAY to you

Country Fresh (Set of 4)
100331 can $23.95 | **US $14.95**

Summer Fun (Set of 6)
101548 can $31.95 | **US $19.95**

SPLASH

Chelsea had two favorites at the water park: floating around and around the canal and playing under the waterfall. I thought she'd get tired and cranky long before she finally fell asleep in Dad's lap, but she just kept going and going and going.

Hope today tickles you pink!

Happy Bird Day!

Tickled Pink (Set of 6)
103205 can $36.95 | **US $22.95**

100353 Stampin' Around® **Pink Flamingo** can $9.50 | **US $5.95** (Wheel only. Handle and ink cartridges sold separately. See pages 204–211.)

Happy
Halloween

Just flying by
with a Halloween Hi!

You give me
a warm glow
inside!

Just flying by
with a Halloween Hi!

Just Flying By (Set of 7)
101867 can $34.95 | **us $21.95**

HAPPY
FROIGHT
NIGHT!

A BATTY
BOO...
FROOM ME
TO YOU!

WITCHING YOU
A
HAPPY
HOWLOWEEN!

HAPPY
FROIGHT
NIGHT!

Tricky Treats (Set of 3)
101407 can $28.95 | **us $17.95**

Bitty Boos (Set of 12)
101679 can $26.95 | **US $16.95**

Trick or Treat (Set of 4)
100028 can $18.95 | **US $11.95**

100267 Stampin' Around® **Happy Jacks** can $9.50 | **US $5.95** (Wheel only. Handle and ink cartridges sold separately. See pages 204–211.)

Costume Bears (Set of 4)
101158 can $23.95 | **US $14.95**

Just a little
Halloween greeting
to wish you happy
trick-or-treating!

Halloween Hedgehogs (Set of 6)
101369 can $31.95 | **US $19.95**

102239 Stampin' Around® **Jack-O'-Lantern** can $9.50 | **US $5.95** (Wheel only. Handle and ink cartridges sold separately. See pages 204–211.)

40 autumn

MAY YOUR HALLOWEEN BE FULL OF SMILES!

Halloween Smiles (Set of 4)
100136 can $29.95 | **US $18.95**

HAPPY HALLOWEEN

Grinning Ghouls (Set of 6)
100251 can $31.95 | **US $19.95**

Amy loves Halloween. She says It is her favorite holiday because she can dress up as anything she wants.

100351 Stampin' Around® **Spooky Spiders** can $9.50 | **US $5.95** (Wheel only. Handle and ink cartridges sold separately. See pages 204–211.)

Spooktacular Greetings (Set of 6)
100859 Can $31.95 | **US $19.95**

Fall Fun (Set of 6)
100675 Can $23.95 | **US $14.95**

100514 Stampin' Around® **Harvest** Can $9.50 | **US $5.95** (Wheel only. Handle and ink cartridges sold separately. See pages 204–211.)

Happy Fall Y'all (Set of 7)
100961 can $31.95 | **US $19.95**

thanks for your kindness

AWESOME AUTUMN

Taylor wanted a picture of his pumpkin before he carved it and I knew the perfect backdrop. The colors of the vines this year were spectacular! I love the way these shots turned out. October 2001

Fall Whimsy (Set of 6)
100130 can $23.95 | **US $14.95**

100360 Stampin' Around® **Acorns** can $9.50 | **US $5.95** (Wheel only. Handle and ink cartridges sold separately. See pages 204–211.)

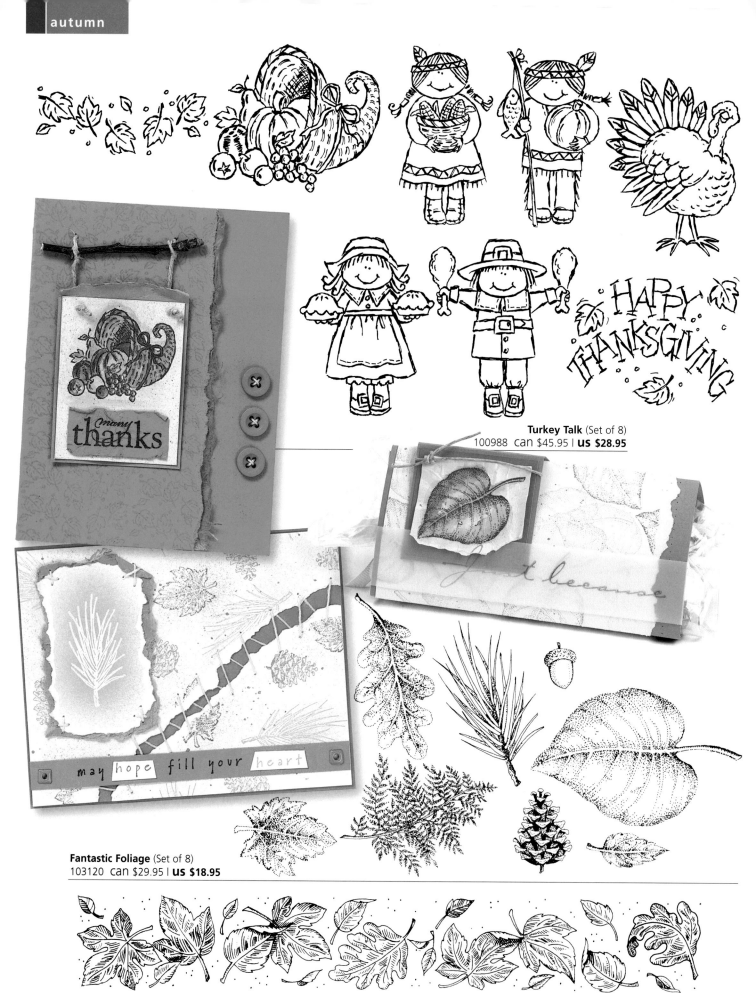

Turkey Talk (Set of 8)
100988 can $45.95 | **US $28.95**

Fantastic Foliage (Set of 8)
103120 can $29.95 | **US $18.95**

many thanks

may hope fill your heart

101909 Stampin' Around® **Swirling Leaves** can $9.50 | **US $5.95** (Wheel only. Handle and ink cartridges sold separately. See pages 204–211.)

Thinking of you
during this
season of thanks!

Season of Thanks (Set of 4)
102214 can $28.95 | **US $17.95**

PERFECT FRIENDS

Thinking of you

This set has a coordinating Classy Brass™ embossing template on page 229.

Festive Fall (Set of 8)
102078 can $34.95 | **US $21.95**

Thinking of you

101095 Stampin' Around® **Fall Frolics** can $9.50 | **US $5.95** (Wheel only. Handle and ink cartridges sold separately. See pages 204–211.)

Happy Hanukkah

Festive Hanukkah (Set of 4)
100347 Can $26.95 | **US $16.95**

Mazel Tov on your Marriage

Happy Rosh Hashanah

Mazel Tov on your Bat Mitzvah

Happy Passover

Mazel Tov on your Bar Mitzvah

Mazel Tov (Set of 6)
100329 Can $31.95 | **US $19.95**

Winter Wonderland (Set of 6)
101972 can $36.95 | **US $22.95**

May Christmas
fill your heart
with a warm
and friendly
light.

*Happy
Holidays*

Sleigh Ride (Set of 6)
100176 can $34.95 | **US $21.95**

To:
From:

Christmas Gift Tags (Set of 8)
101920 can $42.95 | **US $26.95**

Happy Winter (Set of 4)
100789 can $18.95 | **US $11.95**

Christmas Wishes

To:

From:

Old-Fashioned Christmas (Set of 6)
103020 can $45.95 | **US $28.95**

Joy is in the air!

Snow Globe (Set of 7)
101241 can $31.95 | **US $19.95**

joy is in the air!

TO:
FROM:
DO NOT OPEN
'TIL
CHRISTMAS!

Festive Friends (Set of 4)
101286 Can $18.95 | **US $11.95**

MERRY
CHRISTMAS!

TO:
FROM:
HAPPY
HOLLY-
DAYS!

HO!
HO!
HO!

NO
PEEKING
'TIL
CHRISTMAS!

JOY

Holiday Sampler (Set of 28)
102100 Can $47.95 | **US $29.95**

MERRY CHRISTMAS

103296 Stampin' Around® **Candy Cane Christmas** Can $9.50 | **US $5.95** (Wheel only. Handle and ink cartridges sold separately. See pages 204–211.)

HOPING YOUR CHRISTMAS IS COLORED WITH HAPPINESS!

NO PEEKING 'TIL CHRISTMAS!

christmas bear hugs

LIZ, ANNA & JACOB WERE SO EXCITED ABOUT THE GIANT BEAR AUNT KATE SENT-THEY ARGUED OVER IT! DEC. '01

Crayon Christmas (Set of 8)
101239 can $45.95 | **us $28.95**

Season's Sketches (Set of 8)
100674 can $45.95 | **us $28.95**

NOEL

MAY THIS SEASON BRING YOU ONE MERRY MOMENT AFTER ANOTHER!

A Merry Season (Set of 4)
100780 can $29.95 | **US $18.95**

best friends

Happy Holidays!

Happy Holidays!

merry & bright

To:
From:

Some of my best friends are flakes!

Flaky Friends (Set of 8)
101850 can $39.95 | **US $24.95**

100417 Stampin' Around® **Many Mittens** can $9.50 | **US $5.95** (Wheel only. Handle and ink cartridges sold separately. See pages 204–211.)

HAPPY
HO·HO·HOLIDAYS!

Ho-Ho-Holidays (Set of 6)
100142 can $28.95 | **US $17.95**

BEST WISHES
TO YOU
IN THIS SEASON
OF MERRIMENT!

Merry Elves (Set of 4)
100156 can $28.95 | **US $17.95**

103161 Stampin' Around® **Christmas Time** can $9.50 | **US $5.95** (Wheel only. Handle and ink cartridges sold separately. See pages 204–211.)

To:
From:

Merry Christmas

Wishing you good friends & happy memories!

Holiday Hedgehogs (Set of 9)
101682 can **$45.95** | **US $28.95**

To:
From:

may the spirit of Love, the beauty of Hope and the blessings of Peace be your gifts this Christmas Season

Warmest Holiday Wishes

Holiday Wishes (Set of 6)
100426 can **$36.95** | **US $22.95**

To: Kaye

103195 Stampin' Around® **Gifts Galore** can **$9.50** | **US $5.95** (Wheel only. Handle and ink cartridges sold separately. See pages 204–211.)

Happy Holidays

Frosty (Set of 4)
101826 can $26.95 | **US $16.95**

happy holidays

to:

from:

Holiday Woodcuts (Set of 6)
100006 can $31.95 | **US $19.95**

101927 Stampin' Around® **Snowman Fun** can $9.50 | **US $5.95** (Wheel only. Handle and ink cartridges sold separately. See pages 204–211.)

Little baby,
sweet and small,
born to be
the king of all.

May the miracle of Christmas
live forever in your heart.

Miracle of Christmas (Set of 4)
101740 can $26.95 | **US $16.95**

The silent snow possessed the earth
and calmly fell our Christmas Eve.

—Alfred, Lord Tennyson

Wishing you a
gentle season of
peace and love.

Season of Peace (Set of 6)
102998 can $34.95 | **US $21.95**

102598 Stampin' Around® **Bold Christmas Trees** can $9.50 | **US $5.95** (Wheel only. Handle and ink cartridges sold separately. See pages 204–211.)

Christmas Foliage (Set of 9)
100122 can $45.95 | **US** $28.95

Jolly Old Elf (Set of 6)
100247 can $31.95 | **US** $19.95

to:

from:

PEACE

COZY WINTER WISHES

Enchanted Snowflakes (Set of 6)
100249 can $31.95 | **US $19.95**

May the blessings of peace,
the beauty of hope,
and the spirit of love
be your gifts this Christmas season.

COZY WINTER WISHES

The Spirit of Love (Set of 2)
102635 can $28.95 | **US $17.95**

disponible en español

Para ver las versiones de estos conjuntos en español visite nuestro sitio web: www.stampinup.com

101934 **El Espíritu Navideño**

100574 Stampin' Around® **Snowy Trees** can $9.50 | **US $5.95** (Wheel only. Handle and ink cartridges sold separately. See pages 204–211.)

*Friendship is...
the sort of Love
one can imagine
between Angels.*

Love

*wishing you a
Season of peace*

hugs and kisses

Love

Angelic (Set of 6)
100261 can $45.95 | **US** $28.95

103150 Stampin' Around® **Heart Angels** can $9.50 | **US** $5.95 (Wheel only. Handle and ink cartridges sold separately. See pages 204–211.)

Star of wonder, star of night... Guide us to thy perfect light.

Star of Wonder (Set of 2)
100253 can $28.95 I **US $17.95**

Peace on Earth Joy to the World

*Star light, star bright—
a wish
for peace on earth tonight.*

Peace on Earth (Set of 7)
102529 can $31.95 I **US $19.95**

101638 Stampin' Around® **Star** can $9.50 I **US $5.95** (Wheel only. Handle and ink cartridges sold separately. See pages 204–211.)

May the quiet beauty of this season bring you deep joy and warm memories to cherish throughout the coming year.

May the quiet beauty of this season bring you deep joy and warm memories to cherish throughout the coming year.

May the quiet beauty of this season bring you deep joy and warm memories to cherish throughout the coming year.

A Beautiful Season (Set of 6)
100158 can $45.95 | **US $28.95**

101088 Stampin' Around® **Pine Bough** can $9.50 | **US $5.95** (Wheel only. Handle and ink cartridges sold separately. See pages 204–211.)

© 1990–2003 Stampin' Up!

'tis the season

'tis the season

PEACE

Polar Bears (Set of 6)
100742 can $31.95 | **US $19.95**

Lace Snowflakes (Set of 4)
101487 can $23.95 | **US $14.95**

101233 Stampin' Around® **Snowflake** can $9.50 | **US $5.95** (Wheel only. Handle and ink cartridges sold separately. See pages 204–211.)

To:

From:

Kris Kringle (Set of 6)
100343 can $34.95 | **US $21.95**

Wishing you
all the wonder,
joy, and peace
the
season brings.

May Christmas
bring carolers,
holly and snow,
bright twinkling lights
upon your tree...
popcorn for stringing
and mistletoe,
the warmth of
friends and family.

Season's Greetings (Set of 8)
100529 can $47.95 | **US $29.95**

Merry Christmas

Happy Holidays

Season's Greetings

May your
Holidays and New Year
be filled with Happiness!

Thinking of you at this time of year,
and though we are miles apart,
may the special love
that's sent your way
keep us close at heart.

May love
and laughter
fill your season!

100357 Stampin' Around® **Kids' Christmas** can $9.50 | **US $5.95** (Wheel only. Handle and ink cartridges sold separately. See pages 204–211.)

merry & bright

Winter Patches (Set of 4)
102363 can $18.95 | **US $11.95**

Snow Angels (Set of 6)
102692 can $23.95 | **US $14.95**

101140 Stampin' Around® **Winter Kids** can $9.50 | **US $5.95** (Wheel only. Handle and ink cartridges sold separately. See pages 204–211.)

101829 Stampin' Around® **Gingerbread Man** can $9.50 | **US $5.95** (Wheel only. Handle and ink cartridges sold separately. See pages 204–211.)

Handstitched Holiday (Set of 9)
101427 can $45.95 | **US $28.95**

May your holidays be stitched with happiness!

HOPE YOUR HOLIDAY SPARKLES WITH HAPPINESS!

Sparkling Season (Set of 6)
100335 can $31.95 | **US $19.95**

100398 Stampin' Around® **Candycane Craze** can $9.50 | **US $5.95** (Wheel only. Handle and ink cartridges sold separately. See pages 204–211.)

© 1990–2003 Stampin' Up!

Every snowflake
brings to mind
how special
you are - you're
one of a kind!

Miss
you.

Thanks
snow
much!

Thanks Snow Much! (Set of 12)
100976 can $47.95 | **US $29.95**

Holiday Basics (Set of 3)
100110 can $28.95 | **US $17.95**

merry & bright · ho! ho! ho! · 'tis the season · joy · deck the halls

Crazy for Christmas (Set of 4)
100126 can $31.95 | **us $19.95**

Happy Holidays

Have yourself a merry little Christmas!

Sending a little wish for a lot of joy!

Little Holiday Wishes (Set of 12)
100150 can $26.95 | **us $16.95**

Happy Holidays

Warm Winter Wishes

Snowflakes (Set of 6)
101589 can $34.95 | **US $21.95**

Warm Winter Wishes

Snow Much fun

Snow Much fun

a happy hello

Snowy Play (Set of 4)
100341 can $29.95 | **US $18.95**

Holiday Print (Set of 1)
100313 can $26.95 | **US $16.95**

May the Gift of Love
be yours this Christmas Season
and always.

What can I give Him,
Poor as I am?
If I were a shepherd
I would bring a lamb,
If I were a wise man,
I would do my part,
Yet what I can,
I give Him...
I give Him my heart.

-C. Rossetti

The Gift of Love (Set of 4)
100281 can $28.95 | **US $17.95**

May the Gift of Love
be yours this Christmas Season
and always.

What can I give Him,
Poor as I am?
If I were a shepherd
I would bring a lamb,
If I were a wise man,
I would do my part,
Yet what I can,
I give Him...
I give Him my heart.

-C. Rossetti

May this holiday
find you
surrounded
by those you love.

Thanks!

Just a little note
to let you know
how much your
kindness
means to me.

Sketch It (Set of 12)
103311 can $55.95 | **US $34.95**

Definitely Decorative® **Fancy Foliage** (Set of 4)
100297 can $39.95 I **US $24.95**

Sun-Ripened (Set of 3)
101943 can $28.95 | **US $17.95**

HUSBAND, WIFE...HAPPY LIFE

Thanks

Thanks

© 2000 STAMPIN' UP!

Autumn (Set of 5)
102674 can $34.95 | **US 21.95**

Sun-Ripened II (Set of 3)
100887 can $28.95 | **US $17.95**

Changing Seasons (Set of 4)
100120 can $42.95 | **US $26.95**

Lovely As a Tree (Set of 6)
101223 can $39.95 | **US $24.95**

Nature

LEAVE A LEGACY

thinking OF YOU

Definitely Decorative® **Pinecones** (Set of 2)
101356 can $28.95 | **US $17.95**

Country Pleasures (Set of 3)
100323 can $28.95 | **US $17.95**

HAPPY
Thanksgiving

for you

THANK YOU

GREETINGS

GREETINGS
of the
SEASON

THINKING OF YOU

THANK YOU

Etruscan (Set of 14)
100943 can $45.95 | **US $28.95**

100355 Stampin' Around® **Etruscan Vine** can $9.50 | **US $5.95** (Wheel only. Handle and ink cartridges sold separately. See pages 204–211.)

Thinking of you
is something nice
I do for myself.

Jump Right In

Madison couldn't wait until daddy raked the leaves into a big pile so she could jump right in. She spent hours playing!

Thinking of you
is something nice
I do for myself.

Something Nice (Set of 6)
102062 can $39.95 | **US $24.95**

THANK YOU!

Thank You Blocks (Set of 4)
102138 can $18.95 | **US $11.95**

Bold Basics (Set of 11)
103178 can $39.95 | **US $24.95**

thanks

you make me smile

CELEBRATE THE SEASON

Little Layers II (Set of 8)
100030 can $31.95 | **US $19.95**

© 1990–2003 Stampin' Up!

Favorite Teddy Bear (Set of 15)
103361 can $47.95 | **US $29.95**

101090 Stampin' Around® **Paw Tracks** can $9.50 | **US $5.95** (Wheel only. Handle and ink cartridges sold separately. See pages 204–211.)

Tags & More (Set of 8)
101380 can $31.95 | **US $19.95**

Little Somethings (Set of 12)
101635 can $23.95 | **US $14.95**

A Tree for All Seasons (Set of 4)
102744 can $18.95 | **US $11.95**

102604 Stampin' Around® **Pindot** can $9.50 | **US $5.95** (Wheel only. Handle and ink cartridges sold separately. See pages 204–211.)

for you

Thanks

Thanks for you

Watercolor Fun (Set of 6)
102567 can $42.95 I **US $26.95**

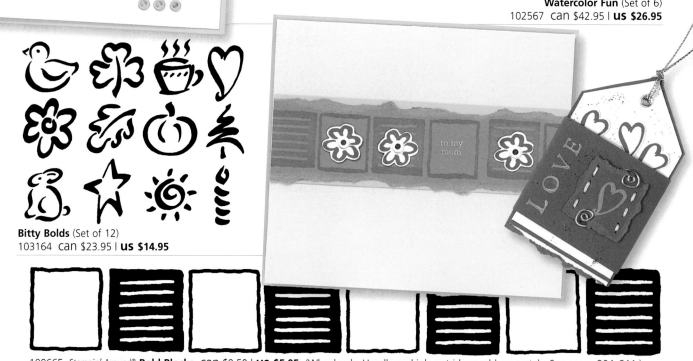

Bitty Bolds (Set of 12)
103164 can $23.95 I **US $14.95**

LOVE

to my mom

100665 Stampin' Around® **Bold Blocks** can $9.50 I **US $5.95** (Wheel only. Handle and ink cartridges sold separately. See pages 204–211.)

it's your day!

Tropical Blossoms (Set of 13)
102093 can $42.95 | **US $26.95**

a happy hello

Happy Anniversary

Fresh Flowers (Set of 9)
102751 can $39.95 | **US $24.95**

don't miss it!

This set has a coordinating Classy Brass™ embossing template on page 229.

103112 Stampin' Around® **Blossoms & Bugs** can $9.50 | **US $5.95** (Wheel only. Handle and ink cartridges sold separately. See pages 204–211.)

© 1990–2003 Stampin' Up!

Thanks for touching my life with your special friendship!

Watercolor Garden (Set of 13)
101352 can $42.95 | **US $26.95**

Thanks for touching my life with your special friendship!

LOVE

warmest wishes

Watercolor Minis (Set of 12)
102846 can $28.95 | **US $17.95**

Memory
is
the power
to gather
roses
in winter

The fragrance lingers
in the hand that gives the rose.

Definitely Decorative® **Roses in Winter** (Set of 9)
100386 can $45.95 | **US $28.95**

FRIEND

Happy *Mother's Day*

*ssus poeticus, Caladium comes
la, Begonia pearcei, Zinnia
ia maculata, Crocus indiflori
cardinalis, Hyacinthus, Tuly
num concolor, Wistaria chine.
ia comta superba, Orchis mac
iflora caerulea, Rosa noisetti
nia thunbergia, Hydrangea hor,*

To Someone Special

To Someone Special

To Someone Special

Botanicals (Set of 9)
101642 can $45.95 | **US $28.95**

Definitely Decorative® **Vine & Berry** (Set of 3)
100192 can $26.95 | **US $16.95**

hugs and kisses

LOVE

Chad & Angie

PERFECT FRIENDS

Fanciful Flowers (Set of 13)
103327 can $42.95 | **US $26.95**

don't miss it!

This set has a coordinating Classy Brass™ embossing template on page 229.

Terrific Tulips (Set of 9)
102783 can $39.95 | **US $24.95**

don't miss it!

This set has a coordinating Classy Brass™ embossing template on page 229.

Definitely Decorative® **Daisy** (Set of 13)
101486 can $47.95 | **US $29.95**

102422 Stampin' Around® **Dots & Daisies** can $9.50 | **US $5.95** (Wheel only. Handle and ink cartridges sold separately. See pages 204–211.)

fabulous florals

Hand-Painted Petites (Set of 20)
100484 can $45.95 | **us** $28.95

Early Spring (Set of 3)
100384 can $36.95 | **us** $22.95

Elegant Rose (Set of 1)
100255 can $20.95 | **us $12.95**

Stipple Rose (Set of 1)
101960 can $20.95 | **us $12.95**

Stipple Hydrangea (Set of 1)
100797 can $20.95 | **us $12.95**

Bitty Bouquets (Set of 4)
102251 can $18.95 | **US $11.95**

you make me smile

How Ya Bee?

Simply Spring (Set of 8)
103298 can $34.95 | **US $21.95**

100811 Stampin' Around® **Busy Bees** can $9.50 | **US $5.95** (Wheel only. Handle and ink cartridges sold separately. See pages 204–211.)

Definitely Decorative® **Springtime Fun** (Set of 12)
101488 can $55.95 | **US $34.95**

January Carnation

February Violet

March Jonquil

April Sweet Pea

May Lily of the Valley

June Rose

July Larkspur

August Gladiolus

September Aster

October Marigold

November Chrysanthemum

December Narcissus

Happy Birthday

Thinking of you
on your special day
and wishing you
the best of everything.

Flower of the Month (Set of 12)
101084 can $47.95 | **US $29.95**

Happy Birthday Frame (Set of 2)
100632 can $18.95 | **US $11.95**

Garden Fairies

Chelsea was the idea girl behind this years Halloween costumes. The girls wanted to be something fun and colorful, and also to be a group. There was Sara, Jen, Noel, Chelsea, and Brinnley

Oct. 29 '02
Halloween Party

Live well,
laugh often,
love much.

Watercolor Garden II (Set of 9)
102724 can $45.95 | **US $28.95**

Spring Garden (Set of 9)
101857 can $39.95 | **US $24.95**

Perfect Petals (Set of 4)
100327 can $23.95 | **US $14.95**

Simple Florals (Set of 4)
100325 can $31.95 | **US $19.95**

Seeds of Kindness (Set of 6)
100295 can $31.95 | **US $19.95**

100270 Stampin' Around® **Dandelions** can $9.50 | **US $5.95** (Wheel only. Handle and ink cartridges sold separately. See pages 204–211.)

You make the good things in life even better.

Sweet Flowers (Set of 4)
100178 can $26.95 | **US $16.95**

Hope is the thing
with feathers
that perches in the soul
and sings the tune
without the words
and never stops at all.

-Emily Dickinson

Feathered Hope (Set of 9)
102221 can $39.95 | **US $24.95**

Hope is the thing
with feathers
that perches in the soul
and sings the tune
without the words
and never stops at all.

Hope today's a
good day for you...

Lovely Leaves (Set of 6)
100263 can $45.95 | **US $28.95**

Definitely Decorative® **Ferns** (Set of 3)
102572 can $36.95 | **US $22.95**

Definitely Decorative® **Vegetable Garden** (Set of 10)
100291 can $52.95 | **US $32.95**

Your kindness makes my heart blossom!

From the Heart

Your kindness makes my heart blossom!

Heart Blossoms (Set of 5)
100140 can $34.95 | **US $21.95**

just a note

HAPPY
Thanksgiving

Delightful Doodles (Set of 4)
100703 can $18.95 | **US $11.95**

YOU MAKE ME SMILE!

HOPE YOUR DAY IS THE HAPPY-FACE KIND!

HAPPY BIRTHDAY!

Smile (Set of 6)
102654 can $23.95 | **US $14.95**

FOR YOU

Smile Accessories (Set of 6)
102457 can $23.95 | **US $14.95**

Scribbles (Set of 4)
101575 can $18.95 | **US $11.95**

good luck

friends

good times

joy

surprise!

dream

noel

celebrate

smile

shop!

sweet

congrats

he's here

she's here

Good Times (Set of 28)
100116 can $45.95 | **US $28.95**

for you

good times

noel

THANK YOU!

shop! shop! shop! shop! shop!
shop! shop! shop! shop!

THANK YOU!

IT'S YOUR DAY!

ITS YOUR DAY!

Fanciful Favorites (Set of 8)
101628 can $31.95 | **US $19.95**

© 1990–2003 Stampin' Up!

THANKS SO MUCH

THANK YOU

HOORAY FOR YOU!

HAPPY BIRTHDAY

THANK YOU

GET WELL SOON

GET WELL SOON

FROM THE HEART

FRIEND·TO·FRIEND

THANK YOU

HAPPY BIRTHDAY

Nice & Easy Notes (Set of 8)
103039 can $42.95 | **US $26.95**

Para ver las versiones de estos conjuntos en español visite nuestro sitio web: www.stampinup.com
102458 Notas Simples

101429 Stampin' Around® **Splatter** can $9.50 | **US $5.95** (Wheel only. Handle and ink cartridges sold separately. See pages 204–211.)

101100 Stampin' Around® **Double-Line Stitched Plaid** can $9.50 | **US $5.95** (Wheel only. Handle and ink cartridges sold separately. See pages 204–211.)

Darling Dragons (Set of 6)
103066 can $34.95 | **US $21.95**

A Greeting for All Reasons (Set of 14)
100999 can $45.95 | **US $28.95**

stamped from the heart
© STAMPIN' UP!

hand-stamped with love
© STAMPIN' UP!

hand-stamped with love
© STAMPIN' UP!

© STAMPIN' UP!

hand made
© STAMPIN' UP!

Handmade with Love (Set of 4)
103016 can $18.95 | **US $11.95**

HAND STAMPED
© STAMPIN' UP!

stamp art
© STAMPIN' UP!

hand crafted
© STAMPIN' UP!

original design by:
© STAMPIN' UP!

original design by:
Renae
© STAMPIN' UP!

Handmade with Love II (Set of 4)
102840 can $18.95 | **US $11.95**

angel policy

Either of the Handmade with Love sets shown above fulfills the requirements of Stampin' Up!®'s angel policy, which governs the sale of hand-stamped items. Your demonstrator can give you full details.

Best Wishes

Happy Birthday

Thank You

Thinking of You

Simple Wishes (Set of 4)
101167 can $18.95 | **US $11.95**

a happy hello

Happy Birthday

Happy Birthday

Thank you

Thinking of you

Simple Sketches (Set of 12)
102771 can $45.95 | **US $28.95**

Simply Sweet (Set of 4)
100337 can $31.95 | **US $19.95**

you make me smile

WARM AND WONDERFUL BIRTHDAY GREETINGS

Thank You for your patience!

Special Offer!

A gift for you!

THANK YOU ♡ FOR YOUR BUSINESS!

For a great Hostess!

I love what I do... You can too!

Bring a friend!

GREAT ★NEW★ ADDITIONS!

For a great Hostess!

THANK YOU ♡ FOR YOUR BUSINESS!

Business Memos (Set of 8)
102403 can $34.95 | **US $21.95**

never forget... you're never forgotten!

Remember... "Stressed" spelled backwards is "desserts"!

Hang in there!

I'm O.K.... really I am

never forget...

you're never forgotten!

Hang in There (Set of 6)
103052 can $39.95 | **US $24.95**

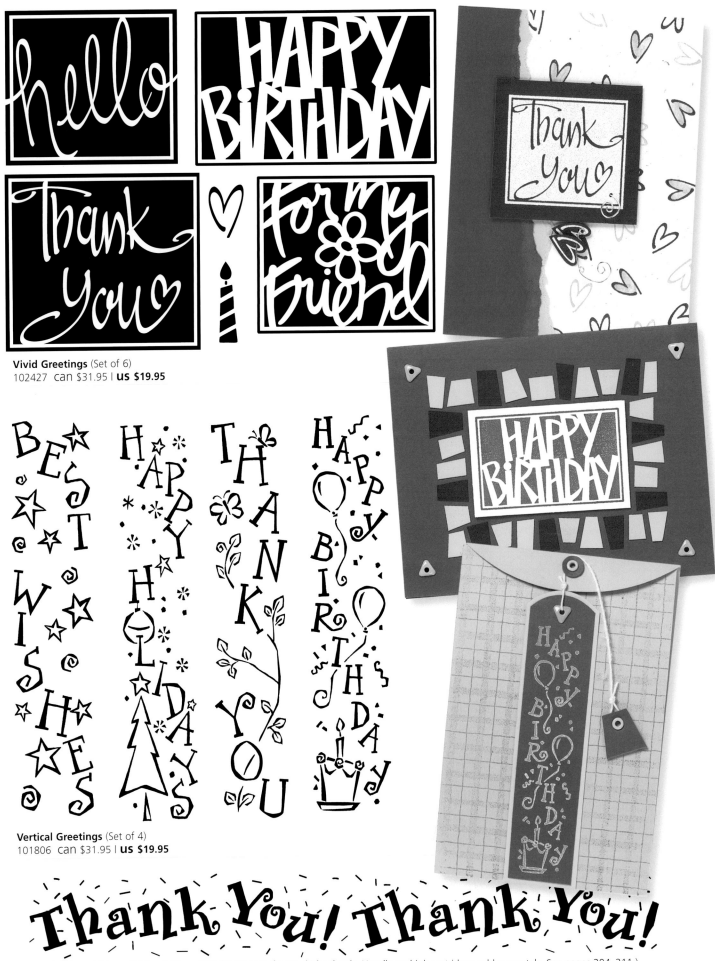

Vivid Greetings (Set of 6)
102427 can $31.95 | **US $19.95**

Vertical Greetings (Set of 4)
101806 can $31.95 | **US $19.95**

101484 Stampin' Around® **Thank You** can $9.50 | **US $5.95** (Wheel only. Handle and ink cartridges sold separately. See pages 204–211.)

Goofy Girls

goofy girls
smiles and giggles
many moods
fun and flirty
laughter and joy
love

FLOWER POWER

GROOVY

FLOWER·POWER·PEACE&LOVE

HIPPIE BIRTHDAY!   FAR OUT

love

Groovy (Set of 9)
102118 Can $39.95 | **US $24.95**

100831 Stampin' Around® **Flower Power** Can $9.50 | **US $5.95** (Wheel only. Handle and ink cartridges sold separately. See pages 204–211.)

You light up my life!

Welcome, baby!

Make a wish!

Just a note

Hang in there!

Wedding Wishes

Get well soon!

For you

I'm Sorry

Just Because

For the Bride

Happy Holidays

You're sweet!

You did it!

Mini Mates (Set of 28)
101027 can $47.95 | **US $29.95**

You did it!

Wedding Wishes

USA

OUCH!

HAPPY HEALING!

DON'T FEEL SO HOT?

HUGS, KISSES & GET WELL WISHES! OPEN CLOSE RX

XO

Hope you're back to your "cool" self soon!

GET WELL SOON!

Happy Healing (Set of 8)
103326 can $31.95 | **US $19.95**

DON'T FEEL SO HOT?

Welcome Baby!

Thank You

Happy Birthday to You...

hello...

To Someone Special...

Miss You...

Thinking of You

Best Wishes

Feathered Friends (Set of 8)
102680 can $42.95 | **US $26.95**

i love you

I Love You (Set of 2)
101008 can $18.95 | **US $11.95**

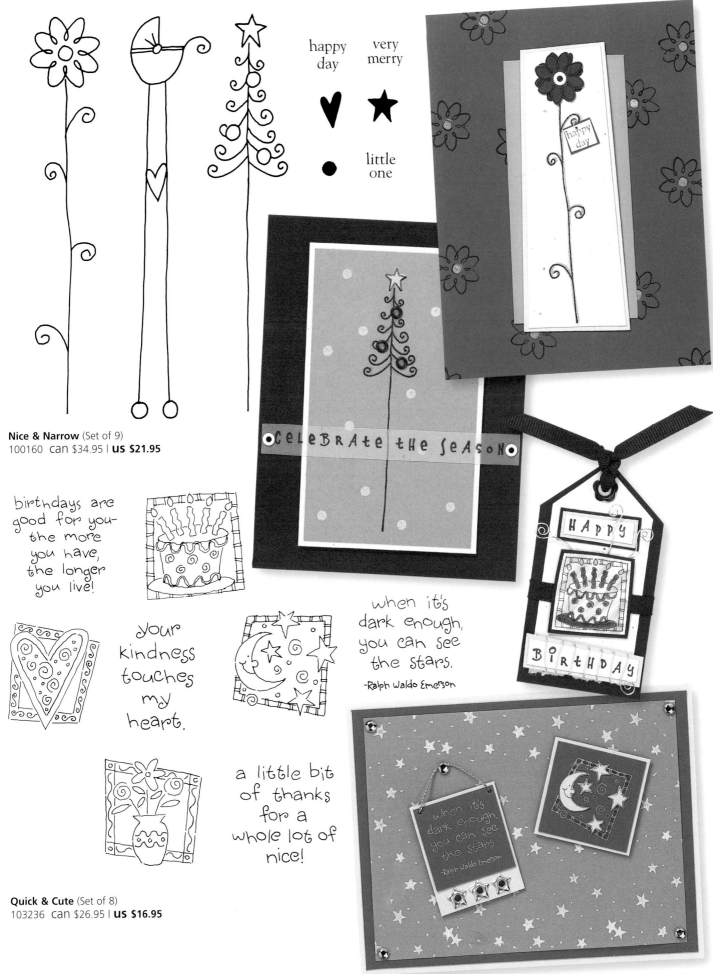

happy
day

very
merry

little
one

Nice & Narrow (Set of 9)
100160 can $34.95 | **US $21.95**

happy
day

birthdays are
good for you-
the more
you have,
the longer
you live!

your
kindness
touches
my
heart.

when it's
dark enough,
you can see
the stars.
-Ralph Waldo Emerson

a little bit
of thanks
for a
whole lot of
nice!

CeLeBRaTe the SeASoN

HAPPY

BiRTHdaY

when it's
dark enough,
you can see
the stars.
-Ralph Waldo Emerson

Quick & Cute (Set of 8)
103236 can $26.95 | **US $16.95**

Many Moos (Set of 4)
100154 can $39.95 | **US $24.95**

Teddy & Friends (Set of 4)
100285 can $31.95 | **US $19.95**

Maine

Oregon

Nova Scotia

North Carolina

Coast to Coast (Set of 4)
103175 can $44.95 | **US $27.95**

FATHER

Thinking of you

for you

Prehistoric Paintings (Set of 6)
100164 can $31.95 | **US $19.95**

for you
for you
for you!

HAPPY FATHER'S DAY

FATHER

Classic Convertibles (Set of 3)
100022 can $28.95 | **US $17.95**

All Aboard (Set of 6)
103165 can $34.95 | **US $21.95**

RIDE ON!

Born to Ride (Set of 6)
100096 can $34.95 | **US $21.95**

BORN TO Ride

HAPPY FATHER'S DAY

Tractor Time (Set of 6)
102017 can $34.95 | **US $21.95**

"A good man
out of the good
treasure of his heart
bringeth forth
that which is good."

Luke 6:45

Letters are visits
When friends are apart.

Write it on
your heart
that every day
is the best day
of the year.

—Ralph Waldo Emerson

Letters from Friends (Set of 9)
102905 can $34.95 | **US $21.95**

Days Gone By (Set of 6)
100518 can $31.95 | **US $19.95**

Parisian Plaza (Set of 6)
100098 can $34.95 | **US $21.95**

i miss you

to: Tony
from: Amber

AIR MAIL

AIR MAIL

Travels Abroad (Set of 6)
100186 can $34.95 | **US $21.95**

Fr. N⁰ 5

Dream Catcher (Set of 6)
103308 can $44.95 | **us $27.95**

Liberty for All (Set of 6)
101568 can $34.95 | **us $21.95**

Friendship is a journey of time, love, and memories.

Friendship's Journey (Set of 4)
100018 can $26.95 | **US $16.95**

World Traveler (Set of 6)
100971 can $28.95 | **US $17.95**

Elegant Ornaments (Set of 4)
100277 can $23.95 | **US $14.95**

Definitely Decorative® **Toile Blossoms** (Set of 7)
100418 can $52.95 | **US $32.95**

Definitely Decorative® **Avian Toile** (Set of 1)
101782 can $26.95 | **US $16.95**

Pastoral Toile (Set of 1)
100315 can $26.95 | **US $16.95**

Sun, Moon & Stars (Set of 4)
101632 can $28.95 | **US $17.95**

Celtic Knots (Set of 4)
100440 can $26.95 | **US $16.95**

Beautiful Batik (Set of 9)
102628 Can $36.95 | **US $22.95**

101282 Stampin' Around® **Batik** Can $9.50 | **US $5.95** (Wheel only. Handle and ink cartridges sold separately. See pages 204–211.)

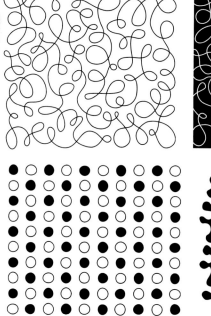

By Design (Set of 4)
100349 can $23.95 | **US $14.95**

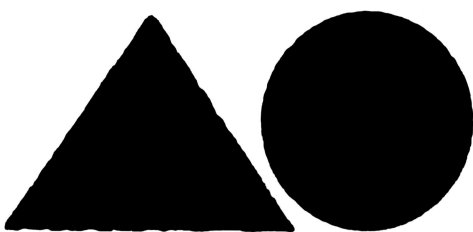

The Shape of Things (Set of 4)
101763 can $42.95 | **US $26.95**

聽
向
你
的
心

Asian Art (Set of 9)
101888 can $47.95 | **US $29.95**

Hang 'in there!

love ('lǝv) n. 1. A deep, tender, and in
feeling of affection and solicitude toward a
uch as that arising from kinship, recogni
attracti   es, or a sense of und
oneness.   (här-mǝ-nē) n. 1. Agre
feeling   harm   A p
combina   s in a whole: co r h
3. The co bination of imulta ous mu   al i
a chord. / peace (pēs   . 1. A state   tran
or quiet.   . The absenc of war or oth host
reedom   disagre nt.
(frend)   attache to ar
affecti   son of roup wi
ne is   or   se:
/ love (A eep,   and i
fe ing of affection and solicitude toward
   h as that ari ng from kin   recogni
 ttractive quali   of underlying
/ harmony ('hä   Agreement in f
accord: live i   pleasing com
of elements i   lor harmony.
combination of simultaneous musical note
chord. / peace (pēs) n. 1. A state of tranqui

I
Love
You

This set has a coordi-
nating Classy Brass™
embossing template
on page 229.

Little Shapes (Set of 4)
101277 can $18.95 | **US $11.95**

harmony

wisdom

love

tranquility

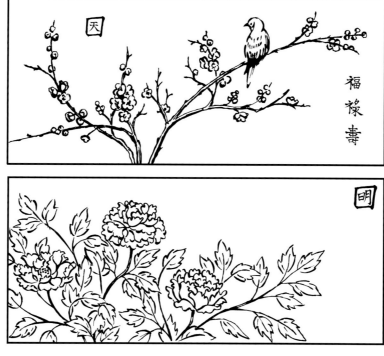

Oriental Paintings (Set of 3)
102602 can $39.95 | **US $24.95**

Kanji (Set of 4)
102081 can $18.95 | **US $11.95**

Art of the Orient (Set of 4)
100339 can $18.95 | **US $11.95**

Definitely Decorative® **Baroque Border** (Set of 2)
102716 can $26.95 | **US $16.95**

100678 Stampin' Around® **Bold Baroque** can $9.50 | **US $5.95** (Wheel only. Handle and ink cartridges sold separately. See pages 204–211.)

WISH SHOE WELL!

SOLE MATES!

MISS SHOE!

GOOD FRIENDS NEVER GO OUT OF STYLE!

CONGRAT ~SHOE~ LATIONS!

Steppin' Style (Set of 13)
101435 can $36.95 | **US $22.95**

CONGRAT ~SHOE~ LATIONS!

RECIPE from the kitchen of Renae
serves 8
Tomato, basil, mozarella Salad
4 large sliced tomatoes
8 oz. mozarella cheese ~ thinly sliced
2 tbsp. chopped fresh basil
olive oil
Capers ~ optional
layer tomatoes and cheese
add basil & capers ~
drizzle w/ oil and serve

SALADS

SALADS

APPETIZERS & BEVERAGES

BREADS

OTHER

MAIN DISHES

DESSERTS

Recipe Fun (Set of 7)
100533 can $42.95 | **US $26.95**

RECIPE from the kitchen of _____
_____ serves ____

LOVE IS A CIRCLE WITHOUT END.

Love

thank you

FRIEND

Park Play

Lauren and kate at The water park! July 2001

Love

Love

Love

Love

LOVE IS A CIRCLE WITHOUT END.

Love without End (Set of 9)
100152 can $39.95 | **US $24.95**

Happy Birthday to You

May peace be your gift this Christmas, your blessing all year through.

A friendship grows forever.

Friendship is a cozy shelter from life's rainy day.

Friendship is a cozy shelter from life's rainy day.

You are one in a Buzzillion...

Babies are bits of stardust, blown from the hand of God. – Barretto

a happy hello

The Fine Print (Set of 6)
100615 can $26.95 | **US $16.95**

© 1990–2003 Stampin' Up!

Happy Mother's Day

Thinking of You

Thank You

Happy Mother's Day

Thank You

Wreath of Roses (Set of 7)
101066 can $31.95 | **US $19.95**

A friend is one who, like sunshine, helps you grow.

Those who bring sunshine to the lives of others cannot keep it from themselves. ~James Barrie

You are my sunshine

You are my sunshine

You are my sunshine

You are my sunshine

You are my sunshine

Those who bring sunshine to the lives of others cannot keep it from themselves ~James Barrie

You Are My Sunshine (Set of 9)
102211 can $36.95 | **US $22.95**

102776 Stampin' Around® **Tulip** can $9.50 | **US $5.95** (Wheel only. Handle and ink cartridges sold separately. See pages 204–211.)

❀FRIENDS COME IN ALL SHAPES AND SIZES, NEED NO ❀ ALTERATIONS, AND NEVER GO OUT OF STYLE!

I LIKE YOUR STYLE!

HAPPY BIRTHDAY TO A SPECIAL SOMEONE WHO'S ALWAYS IN PERFECT FORM!

TO A SPECIAL SOMEONE

I LIKE YOUR STYLE!

HAPPY BIRTHDAY TO A SPECIAL SOMEONE WHO'S ALWAYS IN PERFECT FORM!

I Like Your Style (Set of 7)
100144 can $31.95 | **US $19.95**

Happy Birthday to a Regular Joe!

Your friendship Warms my heart.

friends

coffee break

Just wanted to Espresso my thanks!

Friends are the coffee break in the business of life!

Your friendship

Warms my heart.

Espress Yourself (Set of 9)
101755 can $36.95 | **US $22.95**

Beary best wishes
on your
special day!

A friend is someone
you can lean on.

Beary best wishes on
your special day!

Beary Best (Set of 9)
102714 can $47.95 | **US $29.95**

102347 Stampin' Around® **Teddy Time** can $9.50 | **US $5.95** (Wheel only. Handle and ink cartridges sold separately. See pages 204–211.)

a little
something
just
for you

friends
are like
pockets...
you can
never have
too many!

Pocket Fun (Set of 7)
100162 can $31.95 | **US $19.95**

TO BE A BOY

JOSH WAS IN HEAVEN
RIDING IN THE CARS &
AIRPLANES! AUGUST '02

Plant a seed
of kindness,
gather a bouquet
of friendship.

• for you •

a
little
something
for
someone
special.

with love

with
love

Basket of Kindness (Set of 6)
101106 can $45.95 | **US $28.95**

thank you
very much

thank you thank you thank you thank you thank you th
very much very much very much very much very much ve

Thinking of you is a nice thing to do!

Cute Critters (Set of 4)
101117 can $18.95 | **US $11.95**

Happy Birthday

hello...

Thank you

Happy Birthday

Hedgehog Happiness (Set of 6)
101253 can $31.95 | **US $19.95**

101370 Stampin' Around® **Hedgie Play** can $9.50 | **US $5.95** (Wheel only. Handle and ink cartridges sold separately. See pages 204–211.)

tea for me.

Cassidy's favorite thing to play is "Tea for Me". She sits at the table for hours at a time and serves up cups of water for herself and her dolls.

a happy hello

Definitely Decorative® **Tea Time** (Set of 6)
100279 can $45.95 | **US $28.95**

...frogs & snails & puppy-dog tails...

...frogs & snails & puppy-dog tails...

PUPPIES 4 Love

Little Boys (Set of 4)
102918 can $28.95 | **US $17.95**

Hello

Hello

Fairyland (Set of 6)
100128 can $36.95 | **US $22.95**

Flowers & Friends (Set of 9)
101184 can $36.95 | **US $22.95**

thank you
very much

it's
your
day!

You warm
my heart

You Warm My Heart (Set of 8)
100194 can $31.95 | **US $19.95**

100356 Stampin' Around® **Totally Teacups** can $9.50 | **US $5.95** (Wheel only. Handle and ink cartridges sold separately. See pages 204–211.)

Pretty Peacocks (Set of 4)
100168 can $28.95 | **US $17.95**

it's your day!

welcome, little one

Cold-Weather Friends (Set of 6)
100124 can $29.95 | **US $18.95**

Happy Birthday

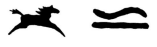

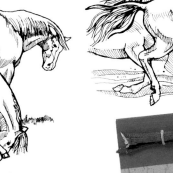

Equestrian Dream (Set of 6)
102809 can $39.95 | **US $24.95**

SPARROW

AMERICAN ROBIN

COMMON
REDPOLL

MEADOWLARK

MOCKINGBIRD

WOOD THRUSH

BIRD
JOURNAL

Bird Watcher (Set of 6)
100104 can $26.95 | **US $16.95**

In the Wild (Set of 6)
100321 can $31.95 | **US $19.95**

see you LaTer aLLigaTor!

In the Outback (Set of 6)
100146 can $31.95 | **US $19.95**

PERFECT FRIENDS

you make me smile

On the Farm (Set of 7)
102203 can $31.95 | **us $19.95**

*O, for a horse
with wings.*
—William Shakespeare

*God forbid that I should go to any
heaven in which there are no horses.*

—R. B. Graham

Brushstroke Horses (Set of 4)
102611 can $29.95 | **us $18.95**

Mandy

101659 Stampin' Around® **Wild Horses** can $9.50 | **us $5.95** (Wheel only. Handle and ink cartridges sold separately. See pages 204–211.)

Definitely Decorative® **Pines** (Set of 6)
100863 can $39.95 | **US $24.95**

101525 Stampin' Around® **Great Outdoors** can $9.50 | **US $5.95** (Wheel only. Handle and ink cartridges sold separately. See pages 204–211.)

good
times

Wolf (Set of 6)
102616 can $36.95 | **US $22.95**

Yukon (Set of 6)
103001 can $34.95 | **US $21.95**

thanks for your kindness

bow wow • ruff • arff

Canine Capers (Set of 7)
100345 can $31.95 | **US $19.95**

you make me smile

it's tough being purrfect

it's tough being purrfect

Purrfect (Set of 4)
100170 can $26.95 | **US $16.95**

arff • bow wow ruff ruff

100361 Stampin' Around® **Playful Pups** can $9.50 | **US $5.95** (Wheel only. Handle and ink cartridges sold separately. See pages 204–211.)

100359 Stampin' Around® **Feline Friends** can $9.50 | **US $5.95** (Wheel only. Handle and ink cartridges sold separately. See pages 204–211.)

Fishy Friends (Set of 6)
100132 can $31.95 | **US $19.95**

you make me smile

HAPPY BIRTHDAY

to you

Definitely Decorative® **Flutterbys** (Set of 10)
102010 can $42.95 | **US $26.95**

don't miss it!

This set has a coordinating Classy Brass™ embossing template on page 229.

102810 Stampin' Around® **Butterfly** can $9.50 | **US $5.95** (Wheel only. Handle and ink cartridges sold separately. See pages 204–211.)

thank you
very much

Stipple Butterfly (Set of 1)
101383 can $15.95 | **US $9.95**

In the Sky (Set of 4)
102344 can $18.95 | **US $11.95**

i miss you

Bunch o' Bugs (Set of 6)
101969 can $26.95 | **US $16.95**

101391 Stampin' Around® **Dragonfly** can $9.50 | **US $5.95** (Wheel only. Handle and ink cartridges sold separately. See pages 204–211.)

Wide Open Spaces (Set of 6)
103106 can $34.95 | **US $21.95**

Bug Builders (Set of 11)
102739 can $39.95 | **US $24.95**

103059 Stampin' Around® **Bitty Bugs** can $9.50 | **US $5.95** (Wheel only. Handle and ink cartridges sold separately. See pages 204–211.)

Thankzzzz!

Cute As a Bug (Set of 6)
103363 can $23.95 | **US $14.95**

Wonderful Wings (Set of 4)
100571 can $47.95 | **US $29.95**

Inspirationals (Set of 8)
100631 can $29.95 | **US $18.95**

I Am a Child of God

Return with Honor

Kindness Begins With Me

may hope fill your heart

welcome

Count Your Blessings

Kindness Begins With Me

Make a joyful noise unto the Lord

Choose The Right

Love is Spoken Here

Jesus is the Reason for the Season

All God's Children (Set of 8)
100283 can $31.95 | **US $19.95**

Two by Two (Set of 6)
100190 can $34.95 | **US $21.95**

Cast thy burdens
upon the Lord
and he shall
sustain thee.
~Psalms 55:22

I thank my God
upon every
remembrance
of you.
~Philippians 1:3

Sing to
the Lord with
thankful hearts.
~Colossians 3:16

Trust in the Lord
with all
thine heart.
~Proverbs 3:5

A friend loveth
at all times.
~Proverbs 17:17

Pleasant words
are as
honeycomb,
sweet to
the soul.
~Proverbs 16:24

With God,
all things
are possible.
~Matthew 19:26

This is the day
the Lord
hath made,
let us rejoice and
be glad in it.
~Psalms 118:24

Say It with Scriptures (Set of 8)
102842 can $31.95 | **US $19.95**

The world is full of suffering. It is also full of the overcoming of it.
—Helen Keller

Hope

Courage is fear that has said its prayers.

Hope (Set of 4)
100561 can $28.95 | **US $17.95**

May the comfort of God's love fill you with hope and peace.

"The Lord himself goes before you and will be with you. He will never leave you nor forsake you."

Deuteronomy 31:8

"A good man out of the good treasure of his heart bringeth forth that which is good."

Luke 6:45

Rejoicing in God's gift of you!

Happy Birthday!

Your kindness is a blessing.

Thank You

"Every good and perfect gift is from above."

James 1:17

God Bless (Set of 6)
102383 can $39.95 | **US $24.95**

WITH GOD, ALL THINGS ARE POSSIBLE.

LITTLE LAMBS, SO WHITE AND FAIR, ARE THE SHEPHERD'S CONSTANT CARE.

THIS LITTLE LIGHT OF MINE- I'M GONNA LET IT SHINE!

WHAT WOULD JESUS DO?

LITTLE LAMBS, SO WHITE AND FAIR, ARE THE SHEPHERD'S CONSTANT CARE.

Little Inspirations (Set of 4)
101595 can $29.95 | **US $18.95**

May the joy of Christ's resurrection live in your heart today and always.

Happy Easter

May our Savior's birth so long ago bring joy to your heart today.

Merry Christmas

Wishing you God's blessings on your Wedding Day!

"I am the resurrection and the life: he that believeth in me, though he were dead, yet shall he live."

John 11:25

"For unto you is born this day in the city of David a Savior, which is Christ the Lord."

-Luke 2:11

"...Neither is the man without the woman, neither the woman without the man, in the Lord."

1 Corinthians 11:11

God Bless II (Set of 6)
101062 can $39.95 | **US $24.95**

CELEBRATE THE SEASON

HUSBAND, WIFE...HAPPY LIFE!

welcome, little one

may hope fill your heart

Fun Phrases (Set of 4)
100134 can $31.95 | **US $19.95**

welcome, little one

thanks
for
your
kindness

HAPPY BIRTHDAY to you

thanks for your kindness

you make me smile

Just because

Simple Sayings II (Set of 4)
100174 can $31.95 | **US $19.95**

MERRY CHRISTMAS

THINKING OF YOU

HAPPY BIRTHDAY

THANK YOU SO MUCH

Greetings 4 You (Set of 4)
102083 can $26.95 | **US $16.95**

Thanks

Good Luck!

Congrats!

Get Well Soon

Happy Birthday

Best Wishes

Happy Holidays

Thinking of You

don't miss it!

This set has a coordinating Classy Brass™ embossing template on page 229.

Bold & Basic Greetings (Set of 8)
102375 can $31.95 | **US $19.95**

© 1990–2003 Stampin' Up!

Best Wishes

Happy Birthday

Thinking of You

Thank You

Just a little note to tell you how special you are.

Sending sincere thanks for your thoughtfulness.

Thinking of you on this special day in a very warm and loving way.

May happiness be yours today and always.

Elegant Greetings (Set of 8)
101163 can $42.95 | **US $26.95**

PERFECT FRIENDS

BETTER GET BETTER
CELEBRATE TODAY!
I think of you
PERFECT FRIENDS

Simple Sayings (Set of 4)
102886 can $31.95 | **US $19.95**

I miss you

Thank you so much!

Happy Birthday

Have A Great Day!

I miss you

Vogue Verses (Set of 4)
101954 can $31.95 | **US $19.95**

Get Well Soon!

Happy Birthday

Thank You

Best Wishes

When everything
is said and done,

being sick
is never fun!

However you may
celebrate,
whatever you may do—
hope your day is
filled with love and
wishes that come true!

Just a little note,
Just a word or two—
Thanking you for
who you are
And everything you do!

Sharing in the
happiness
of your
wonderful news!

Cheery Chat (Set of 8)
102856 can $45.95 | **US $28.95**

May the simple
joys of life
fill this special day
and be yours throughout
the coming year.

Wishing you
merry days,
a heart that's light,
family and friends,
a season bright!

Best wishes
on this
wonderful occasion!

Hoping that each day
finds you feeling
more and more
like your wonderful self!

Your thoughtfulness
warms my heart
and brightens my day!

Wishing you all
the love and happiness
two people can share.

Sending warmest wishes
for a future that will bring
all life's simple pleasures
and the best of everything!

Just wanted you
to know
how special you are!

Versatile Verses (Set of 8)
102226 can $42.95 | **US $26.95**

Happy Birthday

I can't think
of a nicer
person
to celebrate!

HAND-
STAMPED
★
BY

*May this birthday
bring life's
true gifts—
good health,
friendship,
and love.*

Horns to blow,
and bright balloons,
lots of presents,
happy tunes!

WISHING YOU
THE BEST
TODAY AND
ALWAYS!

SORRY I'M
LATE—
HOPE YOUR
BIRTHDAY
WAS
GREAT!

**Happy
Birthday!**

*Happy
Birthday!*

Horns to blow,
and bright balloons,
lots of presents,
happy tunes!

Ice cream, cake,
and candles too—
birthday wishes
just for you!

Ice cream, cake,
and candles too—
birthday wishes
just for you!

Birthday Greetings (Set of 9)
102486 Can $44.95 | **US $27.95**

Happy
Belated
Birthday

Congrats!

Best
Wishes

FOR♥YOU

Happy
Anniversary

Happy
Birthday

Thank♥You

Get Well
Wishes

Favorite Greetings (Set of 8)
100517 Can $31.95 | **US $19.95**

STAMPED WITH LOVE

Your thoughtfulness is greatly appreciated.

Thanks

...for a thoughtful deed in a time of need.

THANKS SO MUCH!

You shouldn't have.... but I'm glad you did!

...for always being there, for listening, and for your love and understanding...

Thank You

Thanks!

Many Thanks (Set of 9)
103156 can $44.95 | **US $27.95**

P E A C E

J O Y

L O V E

it's your day!

Congratulations

many thanks

From the Heart

warmest wishes

thinking O F Y O U

Happy Easter

merry & bright

hugs and kisses

a happy hello

for you

many thanks

All-Year Cheer I (Set of 12)
102189 can $47.95 | **US $29.95**

¡Bienvenido Bebé!

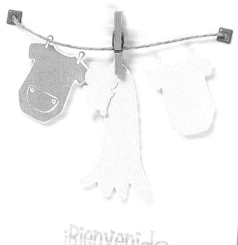

¡Bienvenido Bebé!

Felicidades

GRACIAS

Qué Se Mejore Pronto!

Feliz Navidad

Para Tu Quinceañera

Felicidades en su Matrimonio

Feliz Cumpleaños

Saludos (Set of 8)
102617 can $31.95 | **US $19.95**

You're a great friend!

baby

HAPPY FATHER'S DAY

HAPPY
Mother's Day

Happy Happy Birthday

i miss you

thank you very much

Celebrate!

you're invited

Happy Holidays

for:

on:

at:

by:

to:

from:

You're a great friend!

All-Year Cheer II (Set of 12)
102176 can $47.95 | **US $29.95**

HAPPY

Valentine's Day

Happy
St. Patrick's
Day

Happy
Halloween

Happy
Wedding
Day

Happy
New
Year!

Congrats,
Graduate

good luck

just a
note

to my
mom

HAPPY
Valentine's
Day

HAPPY
Thanksgiving

Happy
Anniversary

Merry Christmas

All-Year Cheer III (Set of 12)
101236 can $47.95 | **US $29.95**

Keeping you close
in thought
and prayer.

May you find comfort
in God's word
and in the knowledge
that others care
and sympathize with you

May the love of God
grant you peace,
the love of friends
bring you comfort,
and the love of
your dear one
live forever
in your heart.

so
sorry...

Hope today's a
good day for you...

and that
tomorrow's
even better.

Blessed are they
that mourn,
for they shall
be comforted.
—*Matthew 5:4*

They are
not gone
who live in
the hearts
of others.
—*Native American Proverb*

With Sympathy

With Sympathy

Hope for Comfort (Set of 9)
103141 can $45.95 | **US $28.95**

Itty Bitty Borders (Set of 4)
100554 can $18.95 | **US $11.95**

merry &
bright

a happy
hello

for you

CARROTS RADISHES CABBAGE

Best Borders (Set of 4)
100406 can $34.95 | **US $21.95**

Petite Patterns (Set of 4)
101717 can $18.95 | **US $11.95**

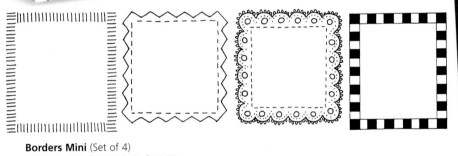

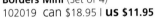

Borders Mini (Set of 4)
102019 can $18.95 | **US $11.95**

Beyond the Basics (Set of 4)
102475 can $18.95 | **US $11.95**

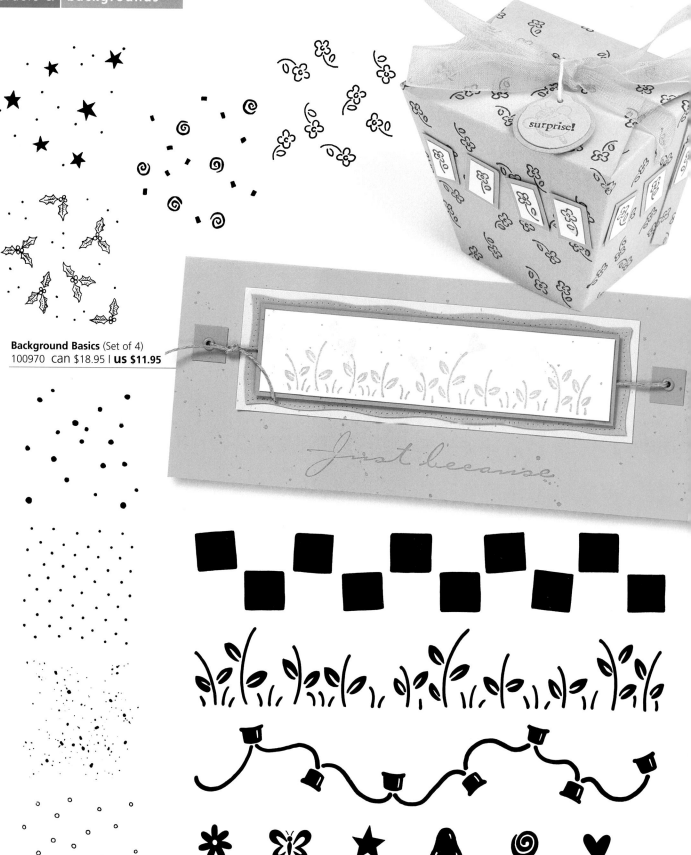

Background Basics (Set of 4)
100970 can $18.95 | **US $11.95**

Itty Bitty Backgrounds (Set of 4)
101893 can $18.95 | **US $11.95**

Border Builders (Set of 9)
102573 can $34.95 | **US $21.95**

just because

surprise!

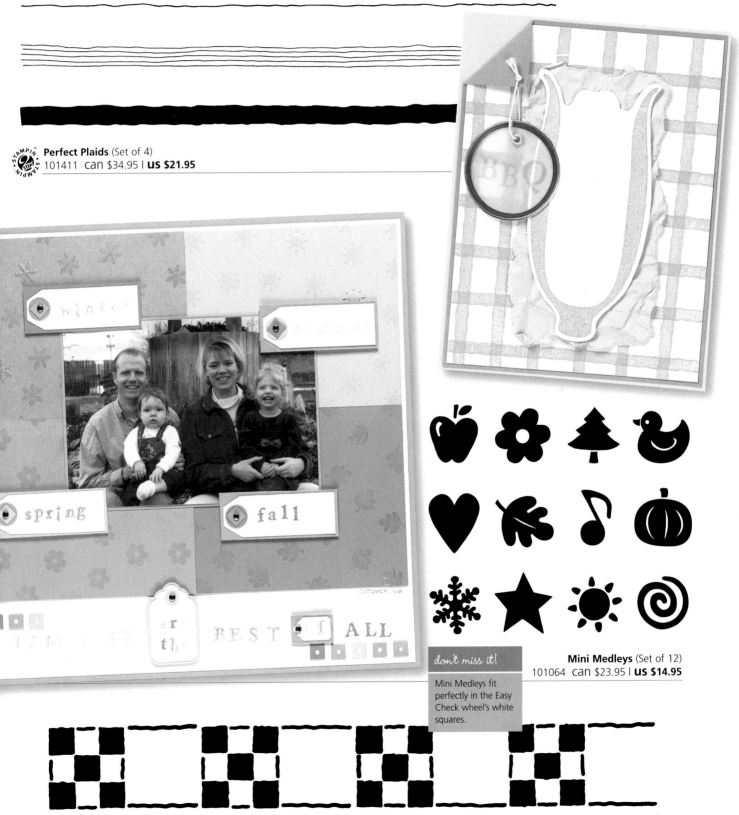

Perfect Plaids (Set of 4)
101411 can $34.95 | **us $21.95**

Mini Medleys (Set of 12)
101064 can $23.95 | **us $14.95**

don't miss it!

Mini Medleys fit perfectly in the Easy Check wheel's white squares.

100941 Stampin' Around® **Easy Check** can $9.50 | **us $5.95** (Wheel only. Handle and ink cartridges sold separately. See pages 204–211.)

Bamboo II (Set of 1)
100275 can $26.95 | **US $16.95**

Filigree (Set of 1)
102784 can $26.95 | **US $16.95**

Antique Background (Set of 1)
100257 can $26.95 | **US $16.95**

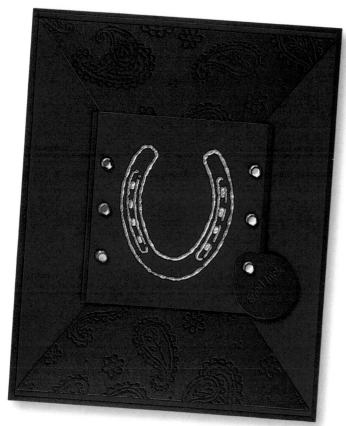

Pretty Paisley (Set of 1)
100166 can $26.95 | **us $16.95**

Swirls & Blossoms (Set of 1)
100182 can $26.95 | **us $16.95**

Groovy Lines (Set of 1)
100112 can $26.95 | **us $16.95**

love ('ləv) *n*. 1. A deep, tender,
feeling of affection and solicitude to
uch as that arising from kinship, r
attractive qualities, or a sense o
oneness. / harmony ('här-mə-nē) *n*. 1
feeling; accord: live in harmony.
combination of elements in a whole: c
3. The combination of simultaneous mus
a chord. / peace (pēs) *n*. 1. A state o
or quiet. 2. The absence of war or othe
reedom from quarrels and disagreem
(frend) *n*. 1. One who is attached t
affection or esteem. 2. A person or gr
one is allied in a struggle or caus
/ love ('ləv) *n*. 1. A deep, tender,
feeling of affection and solicitude
such as that arising from kinship, r
ttractive qualities, or a sense of under
/ harmony ('här-mə-nē) *n*. 1. Agreemen
accord: live in harmony. 2. A pleasi
of elements in a whole: color har

By Definition (Set of 1)
100307 Can $26.95 | **US $16.95**

actual size: Approximate dimensions for all background stamps on pages 164–169 are 4-1/2 x 5-3/4.

Checkerboard (Set of 1)
100594 Can $26.95 | **US $16.95**

Swirls (Set of 1)
101072 Can $26.95 | **US $16.95**

Antique Cracking (Set of 1)
102890 Can $26.95 | **US $16.95**

Musical Score (Set of 1)
101101 can $26.95 | **US $16.95**

Soft Swirls (Set of 1)
100413 can $26.95 | **US $16.95**

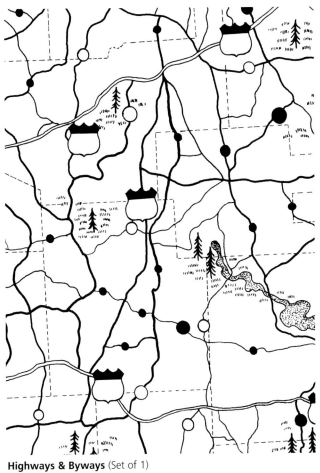

Highways & Byways (Set of 1)
100309 can $26.95 | **US $16.95**

actual size: Approximate dimensions for all background stamps on pages 164–169 are 4-1/2 x 5-3/4.

Vineyard (Set of 1)
100305 can $26.95 | **US $16.95**

Hand-Stitched (Set of 1)
100138 can $26.95 | **US $16.95**

Victorian Lace (Set of 1)
102641 can $26.95 | **US $16.95**

Stipple Plaid (Set of 1)
101446 can $26.95 | **US $16.95**

Harlequin (Set of 1)
101891 can $26.95 | **US $16.95**

French Script (Set of 1)
102086 can $26.95 | **US $16.95**

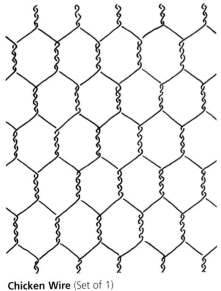

Chicken Wire (Set of 1)
102026 can $26.95 | **US $16.95**

Just Jeans (Set of 1)
100259 can $26.95 | **US $16.95**

good luck

alphabuilders®

AlphaBuilders® (Set of 28)
100934 can $55.95 | **US $34.95**

AlphaBuilders® Accessories (Set of 12)
102233 can $26.95 | **US $16.95**

MASON LOVES ART!
I TOOK THIS PHOTO OF
HIM IN MISS CHRIS' CLASS
ROOM - HE WAS BUSY
SHOWING HIS FRIENDS
HOW TO DRAW A DOG.

FALL 2002

© 1998 STAMPIN' UP!

crazy alphabet

Crazy Alphabet Numbers (Set of 12)
100026 can $26.95 | **US $16.95**

Crazy Alphabet (Set of 28)
100024 can $42.95 | **US $26.95**

crayon fun alphabet

Crayon Fun Alphabet Upper (Set of 28)
100303 can $42.95 | **US $26.95**

Crayon Fun Alphabet Lower (Set of 28)
102368 can $42.95 | **US $26.95**

Crayon Fun Alphabet Numbers (Set of 12)
100766 can $26.95 | **US $16.95**

alphabet fun

Alphabet Fun Upper (Set of 28)
102216 can $42.95 | **US $26.95**

Alphabet Fun Lower (Set of 28)
101355 can $42.95 | **US $26.95**

Alphabet Fun Numbers (Set of 12)
102646 can $26.95 | **US $16.95**

quirky alphabet

Quirky Alphabet Upper (Set of 28)
100539 can $42.95 | **US $26.95**

Quirky Alphabet Lower (Set of 28)
100626 can $42.95 | **US $26.95**

Quirky Alphabet Numbers (Set of 12)
100435 can $26.95 | **US $16.95**

MackenZie is rarely seen wiThouT a cookie in one hand, and more ofTen Than noT, boTh hands! iT's so funny To waTch her, she really savors every biTe! november 2002

alphabet attitude

Alphabet Attitude Upper (Set of 28)
100480 can $42.95 | **US $26.95**

Alphabet Attitude Lower (Set of 28)
102416 can $42.95 | **US $26.95**

Alphabet Attitude Numbers (Set of 12)
101111 can $26.95 | **US $16.95**

alphabet appeal

Alphabet Appeal Upper (Set of 28)
100607 can $42.95 | **US $26.95**

Alphabet Appeal Lower (Set of 28)
102683 can $42.95 | **US $26.95**

Alphabet Appeal Numbers (Set of 12)
103007 can $26.95 | **US $16.95**

We had heard about Scotty's Castle near Death Valley, but had never taken the time to visit. We drove out on a crisp morning, a perfect time of year to visit the desert. January 2003

alphablocks

Alphablocks (Set of 28)
100792 can $42.95 | **US $26.95**

Alphablock Numbers (Set of 12)
101707 can $26.95 | **US $16.95**

little letters

Little Letters (Set of 28)
102103 can $42.95 | **US $26.95**

Little Numbers (Set of 12)
102577 can $26.95 | **US $16.95**

all-around alphabet

double alphabet
All-Around Alphabet (Set of 56 letters, 28 blocks)
102329 can $61.95 | **US $38.95**

don't miss it!
This set has a coordinating Classy Brass™ embossing template on page 229.

All-Around Alphabet Numbers (Set of 12)
103322 can $26.95 | **US $16.95**

brushstroke alphabet

double alphabet
Brushstroke Alphabet (Set of 56 letters, 28 blocks)
102115 can $61.95 | **US $38.95**

Brushstroke Alphabet Numbers (Set of 12)
102711 can $26.95 | **US $16.95**

classic alphabet

Classic Alphabet (Set of 56 letters, 28 blocks)
102528 can $61.95 | **us $38.95**

Classic Alphabet Numbers (Set of 12)
102351 can $26.95 | **us $16.95**

Classic Caps (Set of 28)
102552 can $42.95 | **us $26.95**

bold alphabet

**Aa Bb Cc
Dd ! ?) "**

Bold Alphabet (Set of 56 letters, 28 blocks)
103260 can $61.95 | **us $38.95**

0123#$

Bold Alphabet Numbers (Set of 12)
102149 can $26.95 | **us $16.95**

double alphabets
With these alphabets sets, both upper- and lower-case letters are included. Mount them both on the same block for double the fun! Look for sets marked with:

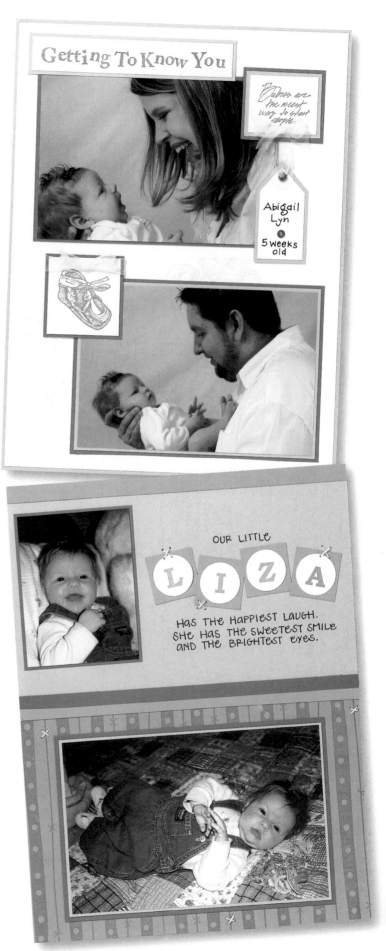

Getting To Know You

Abigail Lyn
5 weeks old

OUR LITTLE
LIZA
HAS THE HAPPIEST LAUGH. SHE HAS THE SWEETEST SMILE AND THE BRIGHTEST EYES.

Congratulations   Thanks to you   Happy Birthday

All Occasions (Set of 8)
101321 can $39.95 | **US $24.95**

THANK YOU!

HAPPY BIRTHDAY

Bold Greetings Mini (Set of 4)
101506 can $18.95 | **US $11.95**

HAPPY·BIRTHDAY!

I'M LEGAL!! FOR MY 21ST BIRTHDAY THE FAMILY GOT TOGETHER FOR CAKE AND ICE CREAM THE BALLOONS WERE MY FAVORITE! GOOD TIMES! JUNE 24, 2002

THANK YOU!

HAPPY·BIRTHDAY!

100552 Stampin' Around® **Happy Birthday** Can $9.50 | **US $5.95** (Wheel only. Handle and ink cartridges sold separately. See pages 204–211.)

Birthday Celebration (Set of 8)
100299 can $34.95 | **US $21.95**

Let's Party (Set of 4)
100148 can $18.95 | **US $11.95**

100358 Stampin' Around® **Party Fun** can $9.50 | **US $5.95** (Wheel only. Handle and ink cartridges sold separately. See pages 204–211.)

HAPPY BIRTHDAY to you

CeLeBRaTe!

Perfect Party (Set of 9)
103029 can $39.95 | **US $24.95**

Happy Birthday

Birthday Balloons (Set of 4)
102302 can $18.95 | **US $11.95**

PARTY

CeLeBRaTe!

100354 Stampin' Around® **Bold Celebrate** can $9.50 | **US $5.95** (Wheel only. Handle and ink cartridges sold separately. See pages 204–211.)

Sketch a Party (Set of 9)
101651 can $39.95 | **US $24.95**

a happy hello

MEGAN

BORN NOVEMBER 24, 2002

Happy Birthday Katie!

A sweet little baby has come from above, bringing joy to your home, filling hearts full of love.

This birthday wish is being sent as just a little token, of warmest thoughts so often felt but all too seldom spoken.

Just My Type (Set of 7)
100301 can $31.95 | **US $19.95**

Like shining lights and tinsel that decorate the tree, our lives are filled with brightness by friends and family.

Sweet Treats (Set of 3)
100180 can $28.95 | **US $17.95**

YOU'RE INVITED!

DATE_____
TIME_____
PLACE_____
FOR_____

RSVP

Dot Invitation (Set of 2)
102534 can $18.95 | **US $11.95**

100268 Stampin' Around® **Whimsical Blossoms** can $9.50 | **US $5.95** (Wheel only. Handle and ink cartridges sold separately. See pages 204–211.)

WARM AND
WONDERFUL
BIRTHDAY
GREETINGS

for you
WARM AND
WONDERFUL
BIRTHDAY
GREETINGS

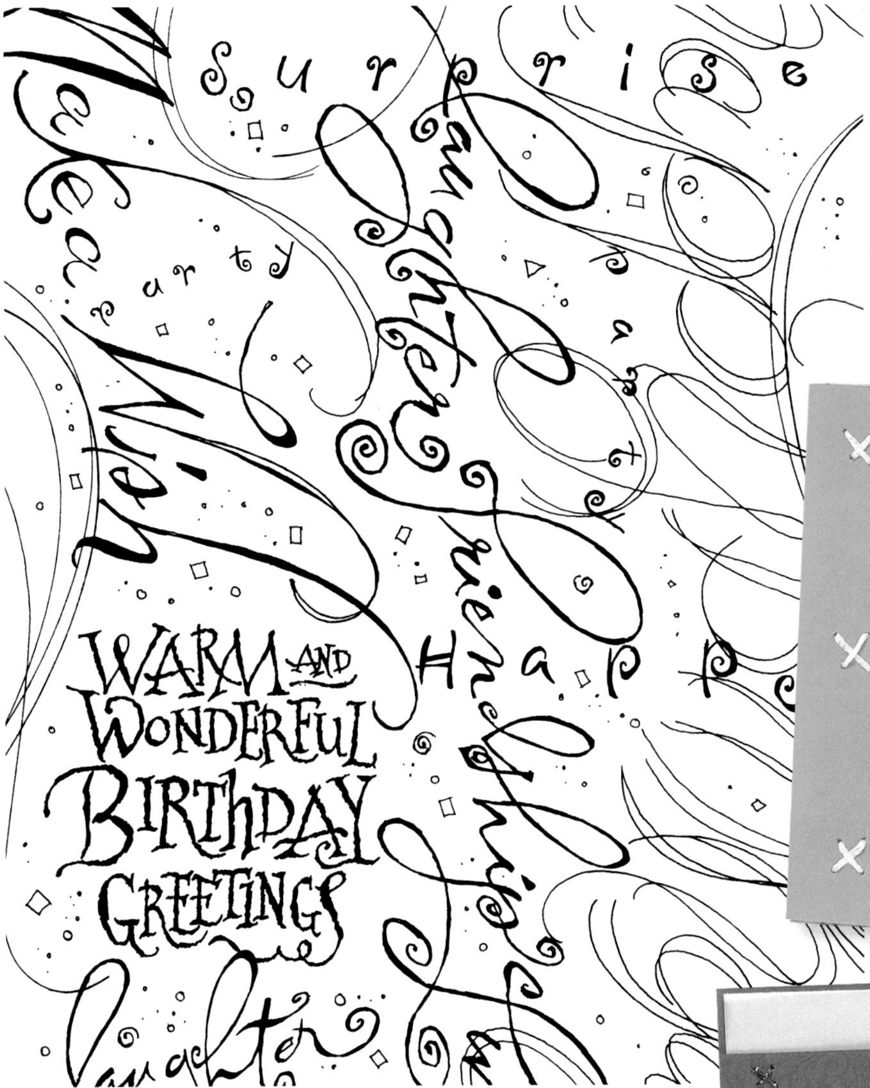

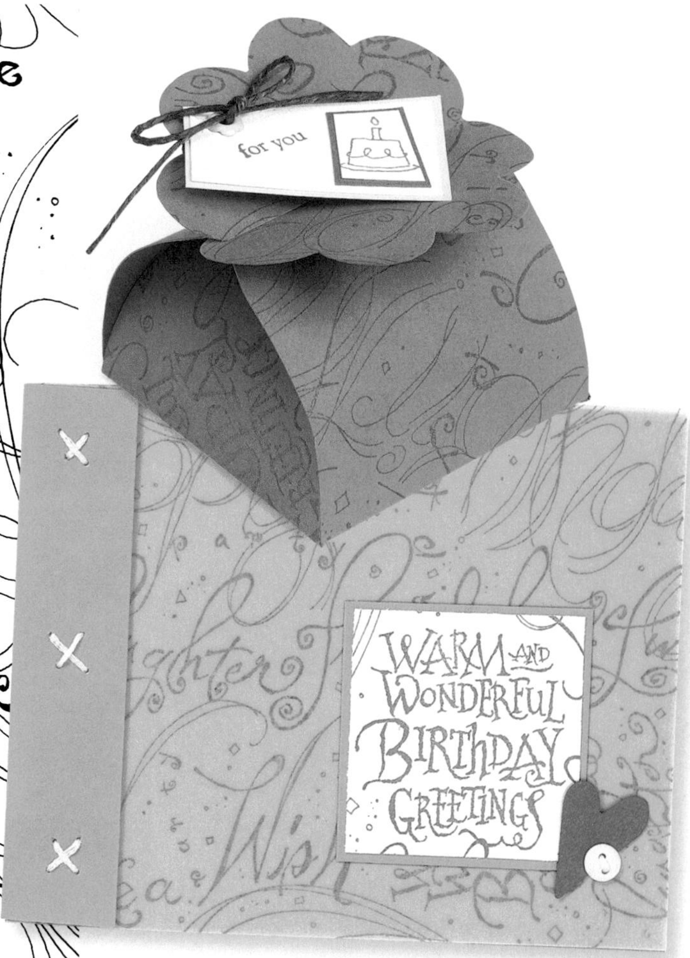

Happy Birthday Greetings (Set of 1)
100311 can $26.95 | **US $16.95**

LOVE
We were married on a Beautiful August morning. The weather was perfect for our reception that evening. Our guests stayed throughout the evening - candle lanterns hung from the trees to illuminate the garden. The flower girls giggled and ran through the small creek in their bare feet. It was the most beautiful day of my life.
August 8, 2001

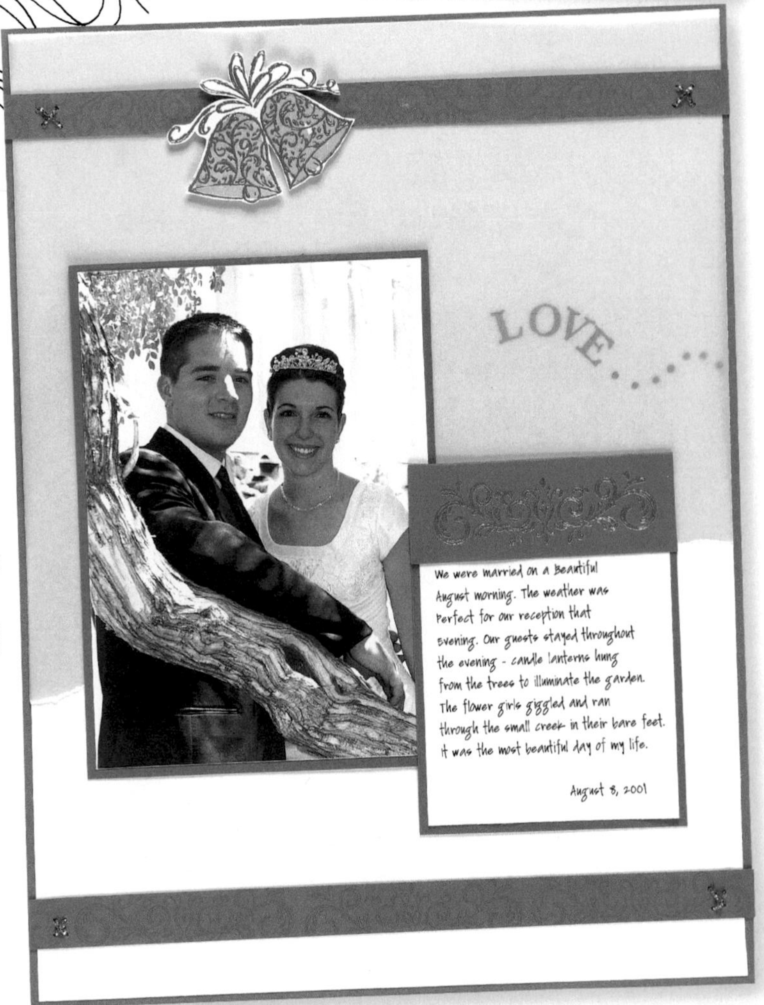

Congratulations
to the
two of you
for choosing
the perfect one.
Wedding
Wishes

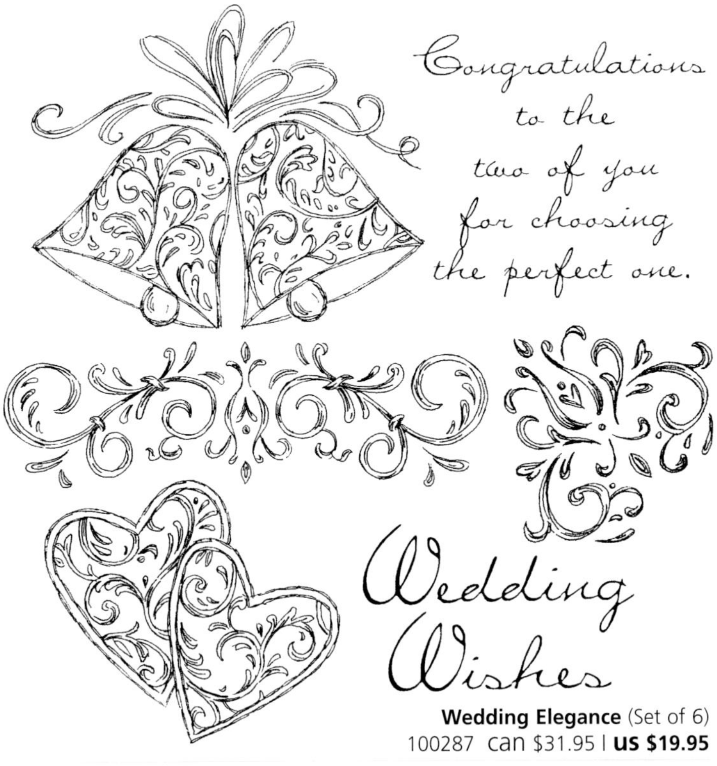

Wedding Elegance (Set of 6)
100287 can $31.95 | **US $19.95**

Congratulations
ON YOUR WEDDING

For the Bride

Hand Stamped

Wishing you a special day of happiness and a love that lasts forever.

A Lifetime of Love (Set of 7)
100457 Can $31.95 | **US $19.95**

For Baby

Babies are the nicest way to start people.

Soft & Sweet (Set of 6)
101700 Can $31.95 | **US $19.95**

100593 Stampin' Around® **Sweet Feet** Can $9.50 | **US $5.95** (Wheel only. Handle and ink cartridges sold separately. See pages 204–211.)

a gift for baby

It's a shower!

for _____
date _____
time _____
place _____
RSVP

for the bride

New Beginnings (Set of 7)
103080 can $31.95 | **US $19.95**

Sketch an Event (Set of 8)
102032 can $34.95 | **US $21.95**

name
born
weight
length
parents

IT'S A
BOY!

IT'S A
GIRL!

A baby is cuddles
And tickles on toes,
The sweet scent
of powder,
A kiss on the nose!

Cuddles & Tickles (Set of 7)
101822 can $26.95 | **US $16.95**

baby

Oaken's FIRST STEP

one

two

three

GO!

Baby Firsts (Set of 8)
102341 can $31.95 | **US $19.95**

.101420 Stampin' Around® **Baby Time** can $9.50 | **US $5.95** (Wheel only. Handle and ink cartridges sold separately. See pages 204–211.)

miss you

the
perfect
pair!

all about ABBY

Abbigail Bonnie Thompson
at 6 months

On the Line (Set of 7)
100008 can $31.95 | **US $19.95**

the
perfect
pair!

It's a
Shower!

Thank
You!

For
You

It's a
Shower!

Happy
Birthday!

Date:
Time:
Place:

For
Baby

You're
Invited!

Para ver las versiones de
estos conjuntos en español
visite nuestro sitio web:
www.stampinup.com

102562 **Acontecimientos**

This set has a coordi-
nating Classy Brass™
embossing template
on page 229.

Announcements (Set of 13)
103188 can $42.95 | **US $26.95**

Definitely Decorative® **Rubber Ducky** (Set of 6)
101660 can $36.95 | **US $22.95**

102144 Stampin' Around® **Checkered** can $9.50 | **US $5.95** (Wheel only. Handle and ink cartridges sold separately. See pages 204–211.)

BETTER GET BETTER

Build a 'Bot (Set of 13)
100118 can $36.95 | **us $22.95**

DINO-MITE! dino park

MAILEY AND DALTON
LOVED OUR VISIT TO
THE DINOSAUR PARK.

DALTON WANTED TO
CLIMB ON THE DINO-
SAURS TO GO FOR A RIDE!

SUMMER 2001

DINO-MITE!

it's your day!

Dino-Mite (Set of 6)
100020 can $31.95 | **us $19.95**

101919 Stampin' Around® **Dinosaurs** can $9.50 | **us $5.95** (Wheel only. Handle and ink cartridges sold separately. See pages 204–211.)

To the Finish (Set of 6)
100184 can $36.95 | **us** $22.95

Yeehaw (Set of 7)
100108 can $31.95 | **us** $19.95

Definitely Decorative® **Choo Choo** (Set of 6)
100293 can $45.95 | **US $28.95**

KID STUFF

Samuel 2002

Crayon Cuties (Set of 6)
102447 can $28.95 | **US $17.95**

MAX

Happy Happy Birthday

Going Somewhere (Set of 4)
101530 can $18.95 | **US $11.95**

100580 Stampin' Around® **Zoom** can $9.50 | **US $5.95** (Wheel only. Handle and ink cartridges sold separately. See pages 204–211.)

Definitely Decorative® **Crayon Kids** (Set of 10)
101135 can $52.95 | **US $32.95**

Definitely Decorative® **Crayon Fun** (Set of 6)
100289 can $31.95 | **US $19.95**

100269 Stampin' Around® **Crayon ABCs** can $9.50 | **US $5.95** (Wheel only. Handle and ink cartridges sold separately. See pages 204–211.)

Teacher Talk (Set of 6)
101558 can $23.95 | **US $14.95**

Teacher Time (Set of 6)
102088 can $26.95 | **US $16.95**

Fun Faces (Set of 8)
101714 can $28.95 | **US $17.95**

I Love Music (Set of 9)
100497 can $34.95 | **US $21.95**

102134 Stampin' Around® **Makin' Music** can $9.50 | **US $5.95** (Wheel only. Handle and ink cartridges sold separately. See pages 204–211.)

Year-Round Fun (Set of 28)
100748 can $45.95 | **US $28.95**

a happy
hello

PERFECT FRIENDS

Kids at Play (Set of 9)
101043 can $39.95 | **US $24.95**

Little Trucks (Set of 6)
102936 can $31.95 | **us $19.95**

Caution: Boy at Work

I NEED A HUG!

Monster Mania (Set of 6)
102097 can $34.95 | **us $21.95**

Dolls are approximately
2-1/2" wide and 4-1/2" tall.

You are the best !!!

sadie and cassandra
have been friends since
the 1st grade. nothing
can separate the two
of them. they are
best friends.

Paper Dolls (Set of 28)
101913 can $47.95 | **US $29.95**
(Includes 12 dolls and 52 items of clothing)

Paper Dolls/Clothes Refill
101432 can $4.95 | **US $2.95**
(Includes 12 dolls and 52 items of clothing)

Paper Pals (Set of 12)
100954 can $31.95 | **US $19.95**
(Includes 12 dolls and 52 items of clothing)

Paper Pals/Clothes Refill
101834 can $4.95 | **US $2.95**
(Includes 12 dolls and 52 items of clothing)

Brian's soccer team won every game this year! He was the most valuable player.

Summer 2002

Dolls are approximately
2-1/2" wide and 4-1/2" tall.

you're invited To a
pack meeTing

where: roger eLLis' house
when: Thursday, march 4Th
Time: 6:30 p.m.
(wear your uniForm)

usa
IS a.o.k.

Friendship Journal

Scouts at Play (Set of 8)
103182 can $34.95 | **US $21.95**

COOKIES

GIRL
POWER

Girl Power (Set of 8)
102644 can $34.95 | **US $21.95**

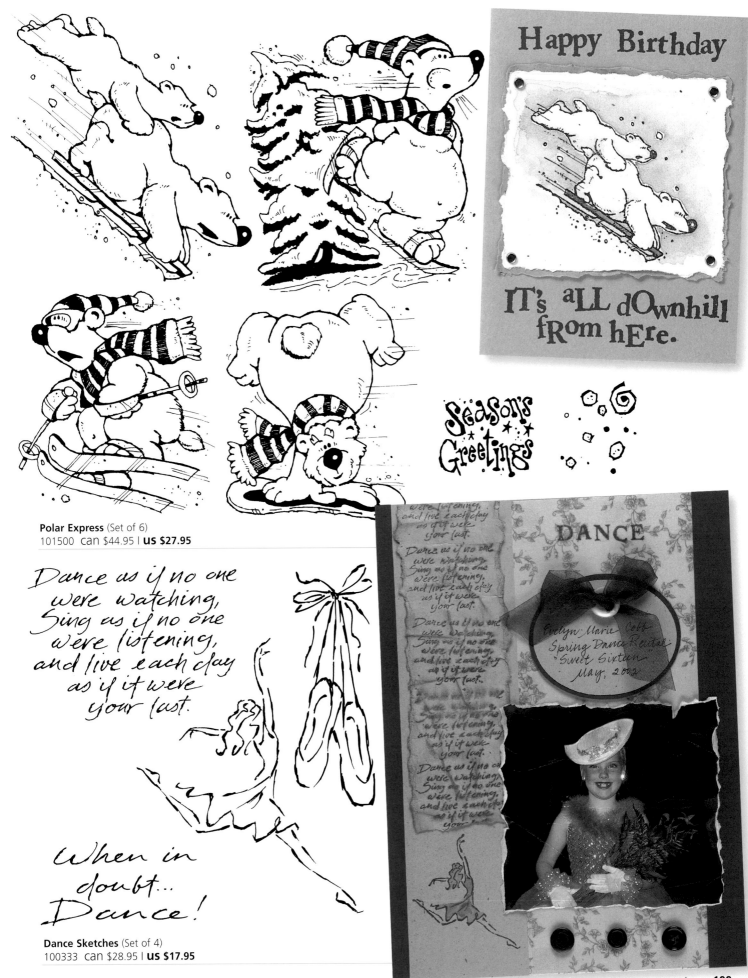

Happy Birthday

IT's aLL dOwnhill fRom hEre.

Polar Express (Set of 6)
101500 can $44.95 | **US $27.95**

Dance as if no one were watching, Sing as if no one were listening, and live each day as if it were your last.

When in doubt... Dance!

Dance Sketches (Set of 4)
100333 can $28.95 | **US $17.95**

DANCE

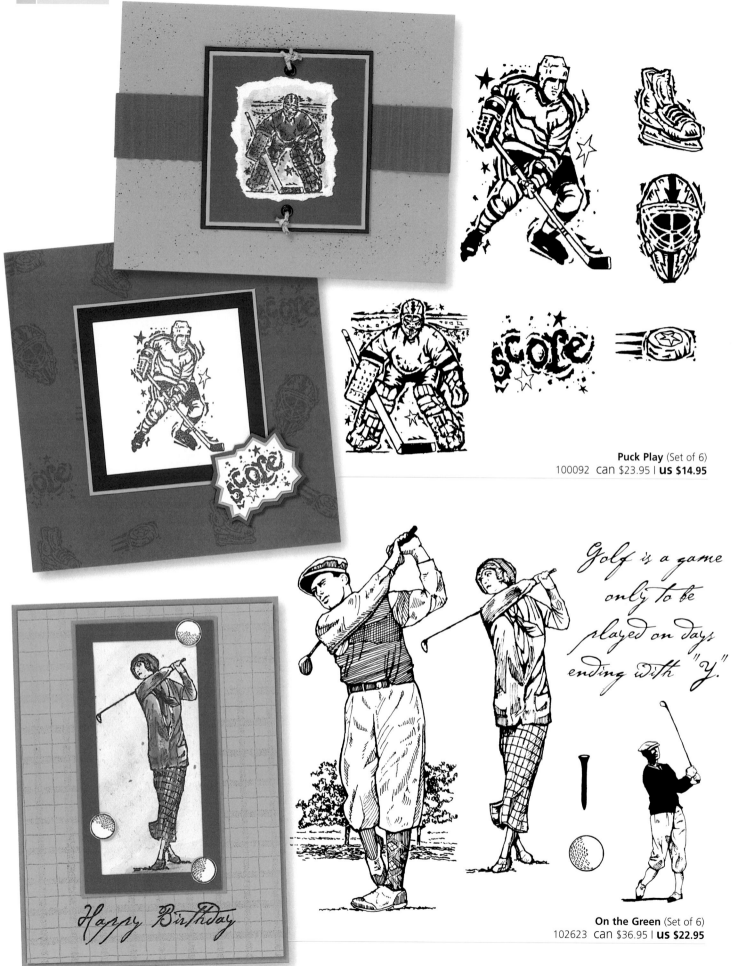

Puck Play (Set of 6)
100092 can $23.95 | **US $14.95**

Golf is a game only to be played on days ending with "y."

On the Green (Set of 6)
102623 can $36.95 | **US $22.95**

Happy Birthday

PLAY BALL

cameron couldn'T sTop Talking abouT how much he Loves playing baseball. This is his FirsT yean playing on a Team, buT i don'T Think iT will be his LasT.

Take Me Out to the Ballgame (Set of 6)
100114 can $36.95 | **US $22.95**

Congratulations

Rough & Tumble (Set of 6)
100172 can $36.95 | **US $22.95**

Stamp your personal belongings and correspondence with Stampin' Up!'s personalized stamps. You can create personal stationery, desktop memo sheets, address labels, and more! Personalized stamps must be ordered on special forms. Please ask your demonstrator for assistance. (No returns on personalized stamps.)

1 "hand-stamped by" stamps

- One line of personalized text (for name)
- Name is in all caps
- Up to 16 capital letters for name (spaces count as a character)

2 text-only stamps

- Up to 32 characters per line (spaces count as a character)
- Capitals and numbers use 2 spaces
- Choose from 1–4 lines of text

3 text-and-image stamps

- Up to 32 characters per line (spaces count as a character)
- Capitals and numbers use 2 spaces
- Choose from 1–4 lines of text
- Font styles and images cannot be interchanged

1 "hand-stamped by" stamp

can $31.95 | **US $19.95**

103516 **"Hand-Stamped By" Personalized Name Stamp**

angel policy

The "Hand-Stamped By" Personalized Name Stamp shown above fulfills the requirements of Stampin' Up!®'s angel policy, which governs the sale of hand-stamped items. Your demonstrator can give you full details.

3 text-and-image stamps can $39.95 | **US $24.95**

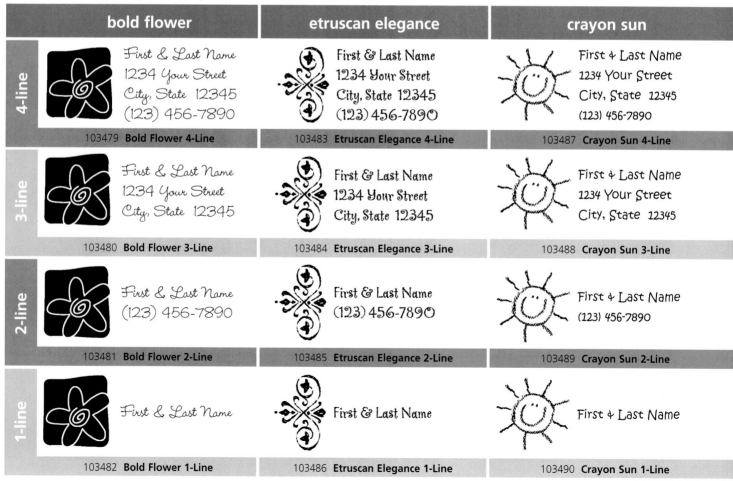

	bold flower	etruscan elegance	crayon sun
4-line	First & Last Name 1234 Your Street City, State 12345 (123) 456-7890	First & Last Name 1234 Your Street City, State 12345 (123) 456-7890	First & Last Name 1234 Your Street City, State 12345 (123) 456-7890
	103479 **Bold Flower 4-Line**	103483 **Etruscan Elegance 4-Line**	103487 **Crayon Sun 4-Line**
3-line	First & Last Name 1234 Your Street City, State 12345	First & Last Name 1234 Your Street City, State 12345	First & Last Name 1234 Your Street City, State 12345
	103480 **Bold Flower 3-Line**	103484 **Etruscan Elegance 3-Line**	103488 **Crayon Sun 3-Line**
2-line	First & Last Name (123) 456-7890	First & Last Name (123) 456-7890	First & Last Name (123) 456-7890
	103481 **Bold Flower 2-Line**	103485 **Etruscan Elegance 2-Line**	103489 **Crayon Sun 2-Line**
1-line	First & Last Name	First & Last Name	First & Last Name
	103482 **Bold Flower 1-Line**	103486 **Etruscan Elegance 1-Line**	103490 **Crayon Sun 1-Line**

2 text-only stamps

| 1-line: can $15.95 | **US $9.95** | 3-line: can $26.95 | **US $16.95** |
| 2-line: can $20.95 | **US $12.95** | 4-line: can $31.95 | **US $19.95** |

classic	contemporary	script
First & Last Name 1234 Your Street City, State 12345 (123) 456-7890	**First & Last Name** **1234 Your Street** **City, State 12345** **(123) 456-7890**	*First & Last Name* *1234 Your Street* *City, State 12345* *(123) 456-7890*
103503 **Classic 4-Line**	103507 **Contemporary 4-Line**	103512 **Script 4-Line**
First & Last Name 1234 Your Street City, State 12345	**First & Last Name** **1234 Your Street** **City, State 12345**	*First & Last Name* *1234 Your Street* *City, State 12345*
103504 **Classic 3-Line**	103509 **Contemporary 3-Line**	103513 **Script 3-Line**
First & Last Name (123) 456-7890	**First & Last Name** **(123) 456-7890**	*First & Last Name* *(123) 456-7890*
103505 **Classic 2-Line**	103510 **Contemporary 2-Line**	103514 **Script 2-Line**
First & Last Name	**First & Last Name**	*First & Last Name*
103506 **Classic 1-Line**	103511 **Contemporary 1-Line**	103515 **Script 1-Line**

sealed with a heart	bursting with love	trio of vases
First & Last Name 1234 Your Street City, State 12345 (123) 456-7890	First & Last Name 1234 Your Street City, State 12345 (123) 456-7890	FIRST & LAST name 1234 YOUR STREET CITY, STATE 12345 (123) 456-7890
103491 **Sealed with a Heart 4-Line**	103495 **Bursting with Love 4-Line**	103499 **Trio of Vases 4-Line**
First & Last Name 1234 Your Street City, State 12345	First & Last Name 1234 Your Street City, State 12345	FIRST & LAST name 1234 YOUR STREET CITY, STATE 12345
103492 **Sealed with a Heart 3-Line**	103496 **Bursting with Love 3-Line**	103500 **Trio of Vases 3-Line**
First & Last Name (123) 456-7890	First & Last Name (123) 456-7890	FIRST & LAST name (123) 456-7890
103493 **Sealed with a Heart 2-Line**	103497 **Bursting with Love 2-Line**	103501 **Trio of Vases 2-Line**
First & Last Name	First & Last Name	FIRST & LAST name
103494 **Sealed with a Heart 1-Line**	103498 **Bursting with Love 1-Line**	103502 **Trio of Vases 1-Line**

Fast and fun, Stampin' Around® wheels are perfect for borders and backgrounds. Handles are sold separately below and inked cartridges in all 48 colors are sold separately on pages 208–211. (Wheels are shown at 50% of their actual size on the next three pages; each pattern is shown full size on the page indicated in parentheses under the pattern.)

stampin' around accessories

a. Self-Inking Handle (Does not include ink cartridge.)

102971   Self-Inking Handle   can $6.50 | **US $3.95**

b. Ink Cartridges & Refills Get beautiful color coordination with the quick and easy fun of wheels! Stampin' Around® ink cartridges come in Stampin' Up!®'s 48 exclusive colors to coordinate with card stock, ink pads, and markers. Color made easy meets stamping made easy! Cartridge refill bottles are specially formulated for use with the Stampin' Around ink cartridges only. Acid free. Inked cartridges in all 48 colors, plus White, are sold on pages 210–211.

102084   Clear Embossing Cartridge   can $7.95 | **US $4.95**

102391   Clear Embossing Ink Refill (1/2 oz.)   can $6.50 | **US $3.95**

Ancient Page™ Permanent ink.

100890   Coal Black Cartridge   can $7.95 | **US $4.95**

101540   Coal Black Refill (1/3 oz.)   can $6.50 | **US $3.95**

Uninked Cartridges These cartridges come uninked, ready to create your own custom color combinations with any of our cartridge ink refills.

101529   Single-Cell Empty Cartridge   can $7.95 | **US $4.95**

102879   Two-Cell Empty Cartridge   can $7.95 | **US $4.95**

102576   Three-Cell Empty Cartridge   can $7.95 | **US $4.95**

don't miss it!

Be sure to check out the *Stampin' Memories Idea Book & Catalog* for an expanded selection of Stampin' Around wheels and scrapbooking accessories, including albums, Simply Scrappin'® kits, and frame stamp sets.

tip

Did you know your 12-inch Paper Cutter can help you create background papers with your Stampin' Around Wheels? Just line up the cutting edge of your cutter with your paper (be sure to put a scratch piece of paper under the whole project) and align your wheel with the edge of the cutter. Start rolling your wheel on the scratch paper and continue across your project and off the opposite edge. Move the trimmer to the edge of the stamped image and repeat. You'll have perfect background papers in no time! Or just do it once to make a great border! (Paper Cutters are sold on page 223.)

102254 Stampin' Around® **Love Swirls** can $9.50 | **US $5.95** (p. 23)

102422 Stampin' Around® **Dots & Daisies** can $9.50 | **US $5.95** (p. 87)

102596 Stampin' Around® **Hugs & Kisses** can $9.50 | **US $5.95** (p. 22)

102776 Stampin' Around® **Tulip** can $9.50 | **US $5.95** (p. 130)

100356 Stampin' Around® **Totally Teacups** can $9.50 | **US $5.95** (p. 137)

100831 Stampin' Around® **Flower Power** can $9.50 | **US $5.95** (p. 108)

100352 Stampin' Around® **Spring** can $9.50 | **US $5.95** (p. 28)

100268 Stampin' Around® **Whimsical Blossoms** can $9.50 | **US $5.95** (p. 180)

102005 Stampin' Around® **Joy of Spring** can $9.50 | **US $5.95** (p. 29)

101773 Stampin' Around® **Star-Spangled** can $9.50 | **US $5.95** (p. 35)

102291 Stampin' Around® **Spring Things** can $9.50 | **US $5.95** (p. 27)

103094 Stampin' Around® **By the Sea** can $9.50 | **US $5.95** (p. 33)

103112 Stampin' Around® **Blossoms & Bugs** can $9.50 | **US $5.95** (p. 81)

100355 Stampin' Around® **Etruscan Vine** can $9.50 | **US $5.95** (p. 75)

100811 Stampin' Around® **Busy Bees** can $9.50 | **US $5.95** (p. 90)

102737 Stampin' Around® **Ivy Vine** can $9.50 | **US $5.95**

103059 Stampin' Around® **Bitty Bugs** can $9.50 | **US $5.95** (p. 147)

101909 Stampin' Around® **Swirling Leaves** can $9.50 | **US $5.95** (p. 44)

102810 Stampin' Around® **Butterfly** can $9.50 | **US $5.95** (p. 145)

100360 Stampin' Around® **Acorns** can $9.50 | **US $5.95** (p. 43)

101391 Stampin' Around® **Dragonfly** can $9.50 | **US $5.95** (p. 146)

101095 Stampin' Around® **Fall Frolics** can $9.50 | **US $5.95** (p. 45)

100270 Stampin' Around® **Dandelions** can $9.50 | **US $5.95** (p. 95)

100351 Stampin' Around® **Spooky Spiders** can $9.50 | **US $5.95** (p. 41)

Wheels are shown at 50% of their actual size.

100267 Stampin' Around® **Happy Jacks** can $9.50 | **US $5.95** (p. 39)

102598 Stampin' Around® **Bold Christmas Trees** can $9.50 | **US $5.95** (p. 56)

102239 Stampin' Around® **Jack-O'-Lantern** can $9.50 | **US $5.95** (p. 40)

100357 Stampin' Around® **Kids' Christmas** can $9.50 | **US $5.95** (p. 63)

100514 Stampin' Around® **Harvest** can $9.50 | **US $5.95** (p. 42)

101233 Stampin' Around® **Snowflake** can $9.50 | **US $5.95** (p. 62)

103161 Stampin' Around® **Christmas Time** can $9.50 | **US $5.95** (p. 53)

101638 Stampin' Around® **Star** can $9.50 | **US $5.95** (p. 60)

101088 Stampin' Around® **Pine Bough** can $9.50 | **US $5.95** (p. 61)

101140 Stampin' Around® **Winter Kids** can $9.50 | **US $5.95** (p. 64)

101829 Stampin' Around® **Gingerbread Man** can $9.50 | **US $5.95** (p. 64)

100398 Stampin' Around® **Candycane Craze** can $9.50 | **US $5.95** (p. 65)

103296 Stampin' Around® **Candy Cane Christmas** can $9.50 | **US $5.95** (p. 50)

103150 Stampin' Around® **Heart Angels** can $9.50 | **US $5.95** (p. 59)

100417 Stampin' Around® **Many Mittens** can $9.50 | **US $5.95** (p. 52)

100665 Stampin' Around® **Bold Blocks** can $9.50 | **US $5.95** (p. 80)

101927 Stampin' Around® **Snowman Fun** can $9.50 | **US $5.95** (p. 55)

102604 Stampin' Around® **Pindot** can $9.50 | **US $5.95** (p. 79)

103195 Stampin' Around® **Gifts Galore** can $9.50 | **US $5.95** (p. 54)

101429 Stampin' Around® **Splatter** can $9.50 | **US $5.95** (p. 102)

100574 Stampin' Around® **Snowy Trees** can $9.50 | **US $5.95** (p. 58)

101100 Stampin' Around® **Double-Line Stitched Plaid** can $9.50 | **US $5.95** (p. 102)

100585 Stampin' Around® **Santa Stars** can $9.50 | **US $5.95**

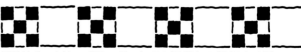

100941 Stampin' Around® **Easy Check** can $9.50 | **US $5.95** (p. 163)

Wheels are shown at 50% of their actual size.

102144 Stampin' Around® **Checkered** can $9.50 | **US** **$5.95** (p. 186)

101282 Stampin' Around® **Batik** can $9.50 | **US** **$5.95** (p. 123)

100678 Stampin' Around® **Bold Baroque** can $9.50 | **US** **$5.95** (p. 127)

101090 Stampin' Around® **Paw Tracks** can $9.50 | **US** **$5.95** (p. 78)

102347 Stampin' Around® **Teddy Time** can $9.50 | **US** **$5.95** (p. 132)

101370 Stampin' Around® **Hedgie Play** can $9.50 | **US** **$5.95** (p. 134)

101659 Stampin' Around® **Wild Horses** can $9.50 | **US** **$5.95** (p. 141)

100359 Stampin' Around® **Feline Friends** can $9.50 | **US** **$5.95** (p. 144)

100361 Stampin' Around® **Playful Pups** can $9.50 | **US** **$5.95** (p. 144)

101525 Stampin' Around® **Great Outdoors** can $9.50 | **US** **$5.95** (p. 142)

101919 Stampin' Around® **Dinosaurs** can $9.50 | **US** **$5.95** (p. 187)

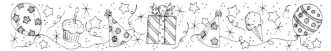

102671 Stampin' Around® **Party** can $9.50 | **US** **$5.95**

100552 Stampin' Around® **Happy Birthday** can $9.50 | **US** **$5.95** (p. 176)

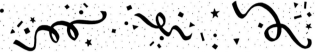

101606 Stampin' Around® **Confetti Streamers** can $9.50 | **US** **$5.95**

101484 Stampin' Around® **Thank You** can $9.50 | **US** **$5.95** (p. 107)

100354 Stampin' Around® **Bold Celebrate** can $9.50 | **US** **$5.95** (p. 178)

100358 Stampin' Around® **Party Fun** can $9.50 | **US** **$5.95** (p. 177)

100593 Stampin' Around® **Sweet Feet** can $9.50 | **US** **$5.95** (p. 182)

101420 Stampin' Around® **Baby Time** can $9.50 | **US** **$5.95** (p. 184)

100269 Stampin' Around® **Crayon ABCs** can $9.50 | **US** **$5.95** (p. 191)

100580 Stampin' Around® **Zoom** can $9.50 | **US** **$5.95** (p. 190)

101046 Stampin' Around® **Super Sport** can $9.50 | **US** **$5.95**

102134 Stampin' Around® **Makin' Music** can $9.50 | **US** **$5.95** (p. 193)

Wheels are shown at 50% of their actual size.

© 1990–2003 Stampin' Up!

Stampin' Up!®'s quality card stock is acid and lignin free—ideal for scrapbooking! It comes in both 12 x 12 and 8-1/2 x 11.

Stampin' Up!'s revolutionary pads feature a flip-top design that stores the inking surface upside-down, so the pad surface stays juicy between re-inkings.

Our Craft Pads contain rich pigment inks that are ideal for scrapbooking, embossing, and other craft projects—they're your best choice for long-lasting color. Our award-winning Classic Pads feature our popular, fast-drying, dye-based inks. Both inks are nontoxic and acid free. (Be sure to order a matching re-inker to keep your Craft pad moist.)

Stampin' Around ink is specially formulated for use only with the Stampin' Around ink cartridges. Order from our exclusive 48 colors on pages 210–211 or see our other cartridge options on page 204.

This tool provides guidelines for creating great color combinations with our exclusive color palette. Even a beginner can combine colors for professional results. It's color made easy!

101513 Color Coach can $15.95 | **US $9.95**

48 Colors

card stock, markers, ink pads, pastels

bold brights

brilliant blue	green galore	orchid opulence
glorious green	yoyo yellow	gable green
lovely lilac	pink passion	positively pink
real red	only orange	tempting turquoise

earth elements

old olive	basic black	chocolate chip
creamy caramel	garden green	cameo coral
more mustard	close to cocoa	going gray
ruby red	really rust	summer sun

See pages 210–211 for ordering information.

All in Stampin' Up!'s exclusive 48 colors!

rich regals

ballet blue	rose red	brocade blue
baroque burgundy	eggplant envy	rose romance
night of navy	bordering blue	marvelous magenta
forest foliage	not quite navy	taken with teal

Delight your color sense with these refillable pastels. Protected in a sturdy case complete with 6 applicators and an eraser. Acid free. (Each color family refill assortment includes 4 colors of chalk. Refill 1 includes colors in the left column of each color family, Refill 2 includes colors in the middle column, and Refill 3 contains the colors in the right column.)

102516	Stampin' Pastels®	can $39.95 | **US $24.95**
103174	Applicators Refill (15)	can $4.95 | **US $2.95**
100852	Pastel Erasers (2)	can $3.50 | **US $2.25**
100241	Bold Brights 1 Refill	can $6.50 | **US $3.95**
100242	Bold Brights 2 Refill	can $6.50 | **US $3.95**
100243	Bold Brights 3 Refill	can $6.50 | **US $3.95**
100238	Earth Elements 1 Refill	can $6.50 | **US $3.95**
100239	Earth Elements 2 Refill	can $6.50 | **US $3.95**
100240	Earth Elements 3 Refill	can $6.50 | **US $3.95**
100232	Rich Regals 1 Refill	can $6.50 | **US $3.95**
100233	Rich Regals 2 Refill	can $6.50 | **US $3.95**
100234	Rich Regals 3 Refill	can $6.50 | **US $3.95**
100235	Soft Subtles 1 Refill	can $6.50 | **US $3.95**
100236	Soft Subtles 2 Refill	can $6.50 | **US $3.95**
100237	Soft Subtles 3 Refill	can $6.50 | **US $3.95**
102476	Real Red Refill	can $2.50 | **US $1.50**
102575	White Refill	can $2.50 | **US $1.50**

soft subtles

barely banana	perfect plum	almost amethyst
bliss blue	lavender lace	mauve mist
mellow moss	blush blossom	pale plum
pretty in pink	sage shadow	mint melody

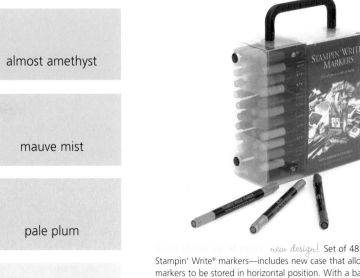

new design! Set of 48 Stampin' Write® markers—includes new case that allows markers to be stored in horizontal position. With a barrel design exclusive to Stampin' Up!, these markers feature a fine tip for details and writing and a brush tip for wider color applications. Each marker is like getting two long-lasting markers in one! Acid free, water-based, dye ink.

100087 **Many Marvelous Markers** can $196.95 \| **US $119.95**

bold brights	classic stampin' pad can $7.95 US $4.95	classic ink refill can $4.25 US $2.50	stampin' write® marker[a] can $4.95 US $2.95	craft stampin' pad can $10.95 US $6.95	craft ink refill can $6.50 US $3.95	8-1/2 x 11 card stock (24 sheets) can $7.25 US $4.50	12 x 12 card stock (20 sheets) can $10.50 US $6.50	ink cartridge can $7.95 US $4.95	ink cartridge refill (1/2 oz.) can $6.50 US $3.95
brilliant blue	100691	100763	100057	101843	103006	100721	102164	100871	102240
gable green	101673	101483	100049	101671	101232	102795	101405	102117	101715
glorious green	103040	101453	100047	101436	100434	101697	102613	102212	102372
green galore	102122	101735	100048	101325	102772	101768	100544	100802	101908
lovely lilac	102874	103077	100056	102965	101695	100427	101601	101256	102315
only orange	102696	102931	100051	101951	102111	102837	102009	101366	102389
orchid opulence	101859	101324	100055	101900	100464	100969	101941	100809	101559
pink passion	101212	102308	100053	102916	103036	102762	102615	102667	103328
positively pink	103122	100944	100054	101157	101630	100734	101386	101725	101783
real red	103133	103287	100052	101190	102104	102482	101554	102996	101684
tempting turquoise	100814	101041	100058	100741	100957	102067	103208	101199	101616
yoyo yellow	102717	101986	100050	101608	103325	102824	101786	102361	102000

earth elements	classic stampin' pad can $7.95 US $4.95	classic ink refill can $4.25 US $2.50	stampin' write marker[a] can $4.95 US $2.95	craft stampin' pad can $10.95 US $6.95	craft ink refill can $6.50 US $3.95	8-1/2 x 11 card stock (24 sheets) can $7.25 US $4.50	12 x 12 card stock (20 sheets) can $10.50 US $6.50	ink cartridge can $7.95 US $4.95	ink cartridge refill (1/2 oz.) can $6.50 US $3.95
basic black	101179[b]	102512	100082	102192	102995	102851	100856	101463[c]	102433[c]
cameo coral	103035	102238	100074	101933	101033	100475	100508	102785	102424
chocolate chip	100908	101065	100071	101816	102847	102128	100623	102496	100767
close to cocoa	103139	102444	100072	100549	100925	101341	101316	100714	101656
creamy caramel	103220	101478	100078	103034	102004	102514	103302	100654	100929
garden green	102272	102059	100080	101841	100519	102584	102651	103252	100684
going gray	103274	102521	100081	102669	103136	103154	100939	101821	101121
more mustard	103162	101962	100076	103092	101990	100946	101566	100566	100873
old olive	102277	100531	100079	103063	101425	100702	101556	102021	100698
really rust	102549	100685	100073	102437	103014	100661	100470	102927	102091
ruby red	102259	100532	100075	101009	102448	102030	103030	102047	100706
summer sun	100537	101231	100077	101690	102765	103124	102480	100660	102913

assorted	classic stampin' pads[d] (set of 12) can $87.95 US $54.95	stampin' spots[a] (set of 12) can $34.95 US $21.50	stampin' write markers[a] (set of 12) can $49.95 US $29.95	craft stampin' pads[d] (set of 12) can $121.95 US $76.95		8-1/2 x 11 card stock (36 sheets, 3 ea. of 12 colors) can $10.95 US $6.95	12 x 12 card stock (24 sheets, 2 ea. of 12 colors) can $12.95 US $7.95		
bold brights	101876	102387	100084	101747	-	101847	101884	-	-
earth elements	102923	103240	100086	102804	-	103060	102495	-	-
rich regals	100465	103116	100085	100454	-	103340	101228	-	-
soft subtles	102542	101968	100083	100819	-	101612	102243	-	-

rich regals

	classic stampin' pad	classic ink refill	stampin' write marker[a]	craft stampin' pad	craft ink refill	8-1/2 x 11 card stock (24 sheets)	12 x 12 card stock (20 sheets)	ink cartridge	ink cartridge refill (1/2 oz.)
	can $7.95 US $4.95	can $4.25 US $2.50	can $4.95 US $2.95	can $10.95 US $6.95	can $6.50 US $3.95	can $7.25 US $4.50	can $10.50 US $6.50	can $7.95 US $4.95	can $6.50 US $3.95
ballet blue	100907	101713	100066	102855	101732	100613	102899	102305	102670
baroque burgundy	102579	103193	100062	101250	101309	102398	101696	100806	102082
bordering blue	102265	100940	100070	101374	102530	102630	101733	101186	102008
brocade blue	101102	100408	100064	101593	100788	101166	101742	103198	100620
eggplant envy	102924	101197	100060	102523	102053	100749	102050	102409	103002
forest foliage	101914	101108	100061	103155	101546	102365	102594	100722	102666
marvelous magenta	101283	101388	100067	102348	102232	102792	103097	102123	102929
night of navy	102977	103033	100069	103181	103131	100867	100653	103027	101772
not quite navy	103008	102949	100059	103227	102310	101722	102443	103084	102581
rose red	101778	102109	100063	101545	102915	102544	102327	100520	103223
rose romance	102092	102519	100065	101539	101191	101991	101724	101112	100540
taken with teal	103257	100550	100068	100617	102049	101584	101176	100460	101360

soft subtles

	classic stampin' pad	classic ink refill	stampin' write marker[a]	craft stampin' pad	craft ink refill	8-1/2 x 11 card stock (24 sheets)	12 x 12 card stock (20 sheets)	ink cartridge	ink cartridge refill (1/2 oz.)
	can $7.95 US $4.95	can $4.25 US $2.50	can $4.95 US $2.95	can $10.95 US $6.95	can $6.50 US $3.95	can $7.25 US $4.50	can $10.50 US $6.50	can $7.95 US $4.95	can $6.50 US $3.95
almost amethyst	101723	102580	100043	101211	102282	102158	100704	100659	102156
barely banana	101170	100639	100039	101609	101676	102701	101929	101516	102121
bliss blue	100769	101765	100046	100960	101138	100510	102665	101314	101726
blush blossom	102609	100614	100037	102080	100935	103318	102814	101678	102801
lavender lace	101305	100862	100041	103144	101590	101614	100905	101812	100501
mauve mist	102618	102731	100042	102699	100451	102901	101762	102861	101147
mellow moss	102774	101771	100038	101054	101967	102898	100638	102871	102194
mint melody	101318	102339	100044	101215	100705	102932	102431	101056	102252
pale plum	102732	101268	100036	103271	102202	101658	101615	101519	102043
perfect plum	101437	102107	100035	102869	100697	101889	101281	101139	102484
pretty in pink	101301	102295	100045	100857	101127	100459	101448	100562	102877
sage shadow	102532	100720	100040	103251	100711	101563	101815	101475	100751

neutrals

For our full line of neutral papers, please see the following page.

				craft stampin' pad	craft ink refill	8-1/2 x 11 card stock[e] (40 sheets)	12 x 12 card stock[e] (20 sheets)	ink cartridge & refill	ink cartridge refill (1/2 oz.)
				can $10.95 US $6.95	can $6.50 US $3.95	can $10.50 US $6.50	can $9.50 US $5.95	can $15.95 US $9.95	can $8.95 US $5.50
white	-	-	-	101731	101780	100730	101874	101460	103017
vanilla	-	-	-	-	-	101650	100467	-	-

[a] Classic ink
[b] The ink in the Basic Black Classic Pad is waterproof and will not bleed.
[c] This ink is not waterproof. For a more permanent ink, choose the Ancient Page™ cartridge sold on page 204.
[d] Comes with sturdy cardboard storage case
[e] Ultrasmooth

neutrals

neutrals	8-1/2 x 11 card stock (40 sheets) can $10.50 **US $6.50**	12 x 12 card stock (20 sheets) can $9.50 **US $5.95**	small envelopes (40) 4-3/8 x 5 3/4 can $9.50 **US $5.95**	large envelopes (40) 4-3/4 x 6-1/2 can $10.50 **US $6.50**	acid free	lignin free	buffered
Ultrasmooth White	100730	101874	101787	101074	•	•	•
Ultrasmooth Vanilla	101650	100467	102293	101701	•	•	•
Kraft	102125	101119	102044	-	•	•	•
Naturals Ivory	101849	102353	103234	-	•	•	•
Naturals White	102316	102841	101640	-	•	•	•

Glossy Card Stock (25 sheets) 8-1/2 x 11

102599 Glossy White   can $7.95 **I US $4.95**

ultrasmooth white   ultrasmooth vanilla   kraft

naturals ivory   naturals white   glossy white

confetti

confetti	8-1/2 x 11 card stock (40 sheets) can $12.95 **US $7.95**	12 x 12 card stock (20 sheets) can $11.95 **US $7.50**	small envelopes (40) 4-3/8 x 5 3/4 can $12.95 **US $7.95**		acid free	lignin free	buffered
Confetti White	102028	102313	102631	-	•	•	•
Confetti Tan	101376	102417	101706	-	•	•	•
Confetti Cream	102835	101409	102610	-	•	•	•

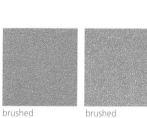

confetti white   confetti tan   confetti cream

specialty

specialty	8-1/2 x 11 card stock (10 sheets) can $10.95 **US $6.95**	small envelopes (20) 4-3/8 x 5 3/4 can $7.95 **US $4.95**			acid free	lignin free	buffered
Shimmery White	101910	102208	-	-	•		
Brushed Metallic Gold	102935	-	-	-	•		
Brushed Metallic Silver	100712	-	-	-	•		

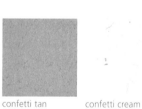

shimmery white   brushed metallic gold   brushed metallic silver

vellum

vellum radiant white	8-1/2 x 11 card stock (20 sheets) can $10.50 **US $6.50**	8-1/2 x 11 paper (20 sheets) can $7.95 **US $4.95**	small envelopes (20) 4-3/8 x 5 3/4 can $11.25 **US $6.95**		acid free	lignin free	buffered
Radiant White Vellum	101856	101839	102075	-	•	•	

Printed Vellum Exclusive Stampin' Up! images, overlaid on fine translucent vellum, make these white-on-white papers an elegant choice! (10 sheets) 8-1/2 x 11

100965 Snowflakes   can $9.50 **I US $5.95**   •   •

101326 Swirls   can $9.50 **I US $5.95**   •   •

radiant white   snowflakes   swirls

tip Use a foam brayer with our Classic Stampin' Pads to make colored vellum in any of our 48 colors! Foam brayers are sold on page 226.

velveteen

velveteen

The rich embossed look of stamped velvet with the ease of paper. (6 sheets, 1 of each color shown)

102157 Velveteen Paper Assortment   can $20.95 **I US $13.25**

mulberry

Mulberry Papers come in colors that work beautifully with Stampin' Up!'s exclusive color-coordinated papers, markers, and ink pads. (10 sheets, 2 each of 5 colors) 8-1/2 x 11

102370	Bold Brights Assortment	can $10.95 | **US $6.95**
100860	Earth Elements Assortment	can $10.95 | **US $6.95**
101693	Rich Regals Assortment	can $10.95 | **US $6.95**
102253	Soft Subtles Assortment	can $10.95 | **US $6.95**

Also available in single colors: (5 sheets) 8-1/2 x 11

103190	Forest Green	can $6.50 | **US $3.95**
101917	Burgundy	can $6.50 | **US $3.95**
102678	White	can $6.50 | **US $3.95**

designer series

Designer Series Papers Sized for 12 x 12 scrapbooks, you can easily cut the sheets down for smaller pages or cards. (10 sheets, 2 of each design)

102204	Candy Paper	can $9.50 | **US $5.95**	• • •
102076	Splash Paper	can $9.50 | **US $5.95**	• • •
101067	Tudor Paper	can $9.50 | **US $5.95**	• • •
102335	Victorian Paper	can $9.50 | **US $5.95**	• • •

Designer Series Vellums Terrific designs based on Stampin' Up!'s exclusive Designer Series Papers! 12 x 12 (12 sheets, 2 of each design)

102037	Candy Vellum	can $17.95 | **US $10.95**	• •
102034	Splash Vellum	can $17.95 | **US $10.95**	• •
102944	Tudor Vellum	can $17.95 | **US $10.95**	• •
101145	Victorian Vellum	can $17.95 | **US $10.95**	• •

acid free   lignin free   buffered

mulberry

bold brights

earth elements

rich regals

soft subtles

designer series

don't miss it!

Be sure to check out the *Stampin' Memories Idea Book & Catalog* for an expanded selection of patterned papers.

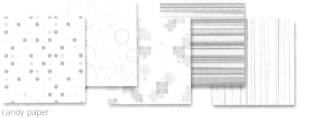
candy paper

splash paper

candy vellum

splash vellum

tudor paper

victorian paper

tudor vellum

victorian vellum

cards & envelopes

a. Greeting Cards with Envelopes (20 per package) 5-1/2 x 4-1/4

101721	Ultrasmooth White	can $9.50	**US $5.95**
103129	Confetti Cream	can $10.95	**US $6.95**
102900	Confetti Tan	can $10.95	**US $6.95**
102014	Confetti White	can $10.95	**US $6.95**

b. Notecards with Envelopes (20 per package) 5 x 3-3/8

101950	Ultrasmooth White	can $7.95	**US $4.95**

c. Raised Edge Notecards with Envelopes (20 per package) 4-7/8 x 3 3/8

101264	Ultrasmooth White	can $7.95	**US $4.95**
102909	Ultrasmooth Vanilla	can $7.95	**US $4.95**

d. Gift Enclosures with Scalloped Envelopes (20 per package) 3-7/8 x 2-3/4

101307	Ultrasmooth White	can $7.95	**US $4.95**

e. Square Cards with Envelopes (10 per package) 5-1/2 x 5-1/2
(Nonstandard size requires extra postage.)

102275	Ultrasmooth White	can $11.25	**US $6.95**

Square Envelopes (20 per package) 5-1/2 x 5-1/2 (Nonstandard size requires extra postage.)

102219	Ultrasmooth White	can $9.50	**US $5.95**

f. Extra Large Envelopes (20 per package) 8-3/4 x 5-3/4   Sized for cards made with a folded sheet of 8-1/2 x 11 card stock. (Nonstandard size requires extra postage).

101097	Ultrasmooth White	can $7.95	**US $4.95**

g. Postcards (25 per package) 5-1/2 x 4-1/4

102031	Glossy White	can $4.95	**US $2.95**

h. Clear Envelopes (50 per package) 4-3/8 x 5-3/4
Assortment comes with 10 each of 5 colors. (Requires extra postage.)

102619	Clear	can $7.95	**US $4.95**
101495	Colored Assortment	can $11.95	**US $7.50**

make your own envelopes!

i. Solid Color Papers Use with the templates shown on the following page for envelopes. Also great for special folds and lightweight layering. Color printed on one side only; reverse is white. Acid free, lignin free, and buffered. (40 sheets, 10 each of 4 colors)

102789	Bold Brights	can $18.95	**US $11.95**
101442	Earth Elements	can $18.95	**US $11.95**
101291	Rich Regals	can $18.95	**US $11.95**
103247	Soft Subtles	can $18.95	**US $11.95**

bold brights: Glorious Green, Real Red, Brilliant Blue, Only Orange

rich regals: Eggplant Envy, Forest Foliage, Night of Navy, Baroque Burgundy

earth elements: Summer Sun, Creamy Caramel, Old Olive, Cameo Coral

soft subtles: Pretty in Pink, Bliss Blue, Lavender Lace, Sage Shadow

templates & stencils

Envelope Template Assortments (set of 3)
Assortment I: note card, small square, and large A-6
Assortment II: gift card, large square, and small A-2

103269	Assortment I	can $19.95 | **US $12.50**
100770	Assortment II	can $19.95 | **US $12.50**

Plaidmaker™ Made with the same durable plastic as our other templates and stencils, these templates can be used with a brayer or sponge to create custom plaids in any color combination. Two templates in each set. Corner slits hold 12 x 12 card stock; works with 8-1/2 x 11 too!

102338	Large Plaidmaker	can $18.95 | **US $11.95**
102697	Small Plaidmaker	can $18.95 | **US $11.95**

Shapes Designed by Stampin' Up!, these stencils coordinate with popular Stampin' Up! images. Use for scrapbooking and papercrafting. All templates and stencils are made of durable, translucent white plastic. For handy storage, choose the Craft Keepers shown on page 222. (12 x 12)

101885	Journaling	can $7.25 | **US $4.50**
100818	Celebrations	can $7.25 | **US $4.50**
101472	Hearts & Stars	can $7.25 | **US $4.50**
100647	Nature	can $7.25 | **US $4.50**
100834	Basic Shapes	can $7.25 | **US $4.50**
102753	Stripes	can $7.25 | **US $4.50**
101175	Seasonal Shapes I	can $7.25 | **US $4.50**
101272	Seasonal Shapes II	can $7.25 | **US $4.50**
101808	Cloud, Moon & Stars	can $7.25 | **US $4.50**

envelope templates

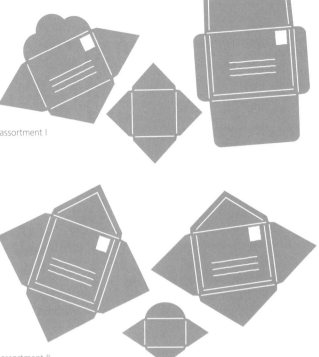

assortment I

assortment II

plaidmakers

large plaid (pair)

small plaid (pair)

shapes

journaling

celebrations

hearts & stars

nature

basic shapes

stripes

seasonal shapes I

seasonal shapes II

cloud, moon & stars

tip
Use any of these templates with the Empressor™ stylus on page 229 to do your own dry embossing!

frames

a. Duo Portrait Frame 10-1/2 x 8-1/2 finished size, 3 x 4-1/2 openings.
Fits 3 x 5 photos.

103337 Duo Portrait Frame   can $9.50 | **US $5.95**

b. Large Portrait Frame 10-1/2 x 12-1/2 finished size, 4-1/2 x 6-1/2 opening.
Fits 5 x 7 photo.

101619 Large Portrait Frame   can $12.95 | **US $7.95**

c. Landscape Accordion Frame 19-3/4 x 7 finished size, 3 x 4-1/2 openings.
Fits 3 x 5 photos.

101469 Landscape Accordion Frame   can $10.95 | **US $6.95**

d. Portrait Accordion Frame 10-1/2 x 4-1/2 finished size, 1-1/2 x 2-1/2
openings. Fits wallet-size photos.

102095 Portrait Accordion Frame   can $7.95 | **US $4.95**

calendars

e. Days to Remember Calendar Give the gift of memories. Scrapbook pages
you create enliven each month. The perforated pages become instant scrapbook pages. It's the ultimate personalized calendar! 8-1/2 x 11

102174 Ultrasmooth White   can $12.95 | **US $7.95**
102286 Confetti White   can $12.95 | **US $7.95**

f. Birthday Calendar Keep track of birthdays and other important occasions
with these perpetual date trackers. 5-1/2 x 15

101398 Ultrasmooth White   can $12.95 | **US $7.95**
100559 Confetti White   can $12.95 | **US $7.95**

assorted paper products

g. Stickers (25 per package) Acid free.

102533 Circles   can $5.95 | **US $3.50**
101141 Rectangles   can $5.95 | **US $3.50**

Sticker Sheets (5 sheets per package) 8-1/2 x 11 (not pictured)

101936 Sticker Sheets   can $7.25 | **US $4.50**

Window Sheets (3 sheets per package) 8-1/2 x 11 (not pictured)

101249 Window Sheets   can $4.95 | **US $2.95**

h. Memo Cube 2-3/4 cube. Blank on 3 sides for stamping.

103062 Memo Cube   can $8.95 | **US $5.50**

i. Vinyl Checkbook Cover (2 per package) Stamp and personalize for
distinctive spending!

101958 Vinyl Checkbook Cover   can $7.95 | **US $4.95**

j. Magnetic Sheets with Adhesive (2 sheets per package) 8 x 10

101705 Magnetic Sheets with Adhesive   can $7.25 | **US $4.50**

tip

We recommend using the quick-drying StazOn™ ink pad on PolyShrink™ to prevent smearing. See page 224 to order.

very merry

crafts

a. PolyShrink™ Make original jewelry, buttons, and charms. (8 sheets per package) 8 x 10-1/2. Assortment contains 2 of each color listed below plus 2 black.

100587	Clear	can $8.95 | **US $5.50**
101334	Translucent	can $8.95 | **US $5.50**
102937	White	can $8.95 | **US $5.50**
102583	Assortment	can $8.95 | **US $5.50**

b. Sanding Blocks (2 per package) The sanding block can be used for much more than preparing PolyShrink. Try rubbing it on our colored paper for an aged effect, or use it to sand a rough edge on your trimmed card stock.

103301	Sanding Blocks	can $5.95 | **US $3.50**

c. Premo Sculpey™ Kit *new!* Add unique dimension to your stamping project with this polymer clay that can be shaped, stamped, and baked. Comes with 3 tools to help shape and cut. Create ornaments, beads, pins, jewelry, or anything else you can imagine. 8 colors, 2 oz. each. Colors: White, Pearl, Cadmium Yellow, Gold, Cadmium Red, Cobalt Blue, Green, and Black.

100244	Premo Sculpey Kit	can $31.95 | **US $19.95**

tip The Sculpey Clay comes with six colors of clay, but you can mix them to create many other great colors! For instance, try mixing black and yellow—you'll end up with a versatile olive-colored clay.

d. Creative Paperclay® Create ornaments, embellishments, beads, and more with this easy-to-use, air-dryable clay. Use sanding blocks shown above to ensure smooth edges.

101872	Creative Paperclay	can $12.95 | **US $7.95**

e. Stamp-A-Mug Change the stamped insert to match your mood or the season!

103313	Stamp-A-Mug	can $6.25 | **US $3.75**

f. Puzzles with Envelopes (10 per package) 5-1/2 x 4

101824	Puzzles with Envelopes	can $8.95 | **US $5.50**

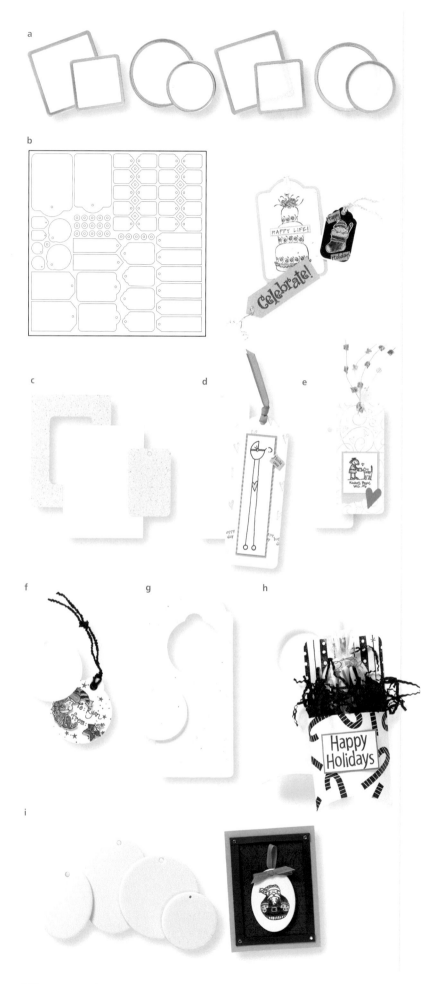

tags and more

a. Metal Edge Tags *new!* You'll love this fun new accent for cards, layouts, or other projects. Available in white card stock or white vellum. Choose circle or square tags. Each package contains six 2-inch tags and six 1-1/2-inch tags.

103372	White Squares	can $6.50	**US $3.95**
103374	White Circles	can $6.50	**US $3.95**
103371	Vellum Squares	can $6.50	**US $3.95**
103373	Vellum Circles	can $6.50	**US $3.95**

b. Tag Sheets *new!* A versatile accent for pages, cards, and much more. 6 assortments to choose from based on our most popular color choices. Each assortment includes six 12 x 12 sheets of die-cut tags, 264 individual tags in all. Layer them or use them alone to add the perfect touch to your project. Color packages include 1 of each color plus Confetti White and Confetti Tan.

100214	Bold Brights	can $10.95	**US $6.95**
100217	Earth Elements	can $10.95	**US $6.95**
100215	Rich Regals	can $10.95	**US $6.95**
100216	Soft Subtles	can $10.95	**US $6.95**
100218	Confetti White & Tan	can $10.95	**US $6.95**
100219	Ultrasmooth White & Vanilla	can $10.95	**US $6.95**

bold brights: Brilliant Blue, Glorious Green, Lovely Lilac, Real Red

rich regals: Baroque Burgundy, Ballet Blue, Night of Navy, Forest Foliage

earth elements: More Mustard, Old Olive, Creamy Caramel, Ruby Red

soft subtles: Barely Banana, Bliss Blue, Mellow Moss, Pretty in Pink

c. Fun Frames & Tags Assortment (48 per package: 12 oval frames and 12 tags, 12 rectangle frames and 12 tags) 3-3/4 x 5

101104	Ultrasmooth White	can $7.95	**US $4.95**
102980	Naturals Ivory	can $7.95	**US $4.95**

d. Large Bookmarks (25 per package) 2-1/8 x 5-5/8

102133	Ultrasmooth White	can $7.25	**US $4.50**

e. Mini Bookmark Sampler (36 per package: 12 Kraft, 12 Cream, 12 Glossy White)

101200	Assorted	can $9.50	**US $5.95**

f. Circle Gift Tags (24 per package) 2-1/2-inch diameter

102985	Glossy White	can $3.50	**US $2.25**
103242	Confetti White	can $3.50	**US $2.25**

g. Door Hangers & Tags (36 per package: 18 doorhangers and 18 tags) 8 x 3-1/2

102199	Glossy White	can $8.95	**US $5.50**
100942	Confetti White	can $8.95	**US $5.50**

h. Door Hanger Pouches (12 per package) 6-3/4 x 3-1/2

102749	Ultrasmooth White	can $6.50	**US $3.95**
102548	Naturals Ivory	can $6.50	**US $3.95**

i. Porcelain Ornaments Create one-of-a-kind keepsake ornaments or tags your family and friends will treasure forever! Use permanent ink for best results. (3 per package) Large Oval: 2-1/6 x 2-7/8; Small Oval: 1-11/16 x 2-3/16; Large Circle: 2-1/2 diameter; Small Circle: 1-3/4 diameter.

102661	Large Oval	can $13.95	**US $8.50**
101739	Small Oval	can $10.50	**US $6.50**
101384	Large Circle	can $13.95	**US $8.50**
102590	Small Circle	can $10.50	**US $6.50**

die-cut boxes & tags

You'll love these fun punch-out boxes in a selection of our 48 colors. Colors included are listed below. We've included tags, which makes these boxes ready-made packaging for every special event. Color packages come with 1 of each color, plus Confetti White and Confetti Tan. (6 sheets per package)

a. Party Favor Boxes & Tags *new!*

100226	Bold Brights	can $10.95 | **US $6.95**
100229	Earth Elements	can $10.95 | **US $6.95**
100227	Rich Regals	can $10.95 | **US $6.95**
100228	Soft Subtles	can $10.95 | **US $6.95**
100230	Confetti White & Tan	can $10.95 | **US $6.95**
100231	Ultrasmooth White & Vanilla	can $10.95 | **US $6.95**

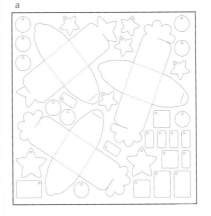

b. Pouch Boxes & Tags *new!*

100220	Bold Brights	can $10.95 | **US $6.95**
100223	Earth Elements	can $10.95 | **US $6.95**
100221	Rich Regals	can $10.95 | **US $6.95**
100222	Soft Subtles	can $10.95 | **US $6.95**
100224	Confetti White & Tan	can $10.95 | **US $6.95**
100225	Ultrasmooth White & Vanilla	can $10.95 | **US $6.95**

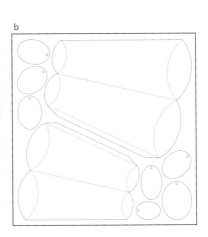

c. Stationery Boxes & Tags *new!*

100202	Bold Brights	can $10.95 | **US $6.95**
100205	Earth Elements	can $10.95 | **US $6.95**
100203	Rich Regals	can $10.95 | **US $6.95**
100204	Soft Subtles	can $10.95 | **US $6.95**
100206	Confetti White & Tan	can $10.95 | **US $6.95**
100207	Ultrasmooth White & Vanilla	can $10.95 | **US $6.95**

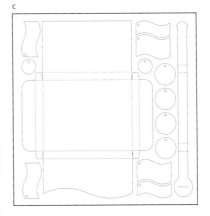

d. Trapezoid Boxes & Tags *new!*

100208	Bold Brights	can $10.95 | **US $6.95**
100211	Earth Elements	can $10.95 | **US $6.95**
100209	Rich Regals	can $10.95 | **US $6.95**
100210	Soft Subtles	can $10.95 | **US $6.95**
100212	Confetti White & Tan	can $10.95 | **US $6.95**
100213	Ultrasmooth White & Vanilla	can $10.95 | **US $6.95**

bold brights: Brilliant Blue, Glorious Green, Lovely Lilac, Real Red

rich regals: Baroque Burgundy, Ballet Blue, Night of Navy, Forest Foliage

earth elements: More Mustard, Old Olive, Creamy Caramel, Ruby Red

soft subtles: Barely Banana, Bliss Blue, Mellow Moss, Pretty in Pink

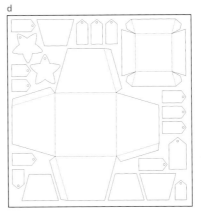

don't miss it!

Be sure to check out the *Stampin' Memories Idea Book & Catalog* for an expanded selection of scrapbooking accessories, including albums, Simply Scrappin'™ kits, and frame stamp sets.

boxes & bags

a. Gable Boxes (6 per package) Large: 8 x 4-3/4 x 5-1/4; Medium: 6 x 4 x 4; Small: 4-1/4 x 2-1/2 x 2-1/2. Assortments contain 2 of each size.

101752	Large White	can $10.95 | **US $6.75**
100493	Large Kraft	can $10.95 | **US $6.75**
100906	Medium White	can $9.50 | **US $5.95**
102595	Medium Kraft	can $9.50 | **US $5.95**
101344	Small White	can $7.25 | **US $4.50**
102332	Small Kraft	can $7.25 | **US $4.50**
102656	Assortment, White	can $9.50 | **US $5.95**
102652	Assortment, Kraft	can $9.50 | **US $5.95**

b. Gift Tote (3 per package) Assembled size: 3 x 6 x 4-1/2. Reverses to Kraft.

102357	White	can $7.95 | **US $4.95**

c. Gift Boxes (3 per package) Small: 2 x 2 x 2; Medium: 3 x 3 x 3; Large: 4 x 4 x 4

102606	Small Kraft	can $4.25 | **US $2.50**
100483	Medium Kraft	can $4.50 | **US $2.75**
103157	Large Kraft	can $4.95 | **US $2.95**

d. Basket Box (10 per package) 3-3/8 x 5-7/8 x 1-3/4

102997	Glossy White	can $12.95 | **US $7.95**

e. Magazine File (3 per package) Assembled size: 9 x 4 x 12

103010	Kraft	can $6.50 | **US $3.95**

f. Lunch Bags (25 per package) 3-1/2 x 6 x 11

100817	White	can $6.50 | **US $3.95**

g. Gift Sacks (3 per package) 4-3/4 x 8 x 10-1/2

100900	White	can $4.95 | **US $2.95**
103321	Oatmeal	can $4.95 | **US $2.95**

h. Cellophane Bags (50 per package) Large Flat: 6 x 8; Medium Flat: 4 x 6; Small Flat: 3 x 5; Large Gusset: 5 x 3 x 11-1/2; Medium Gusset: 4 x 2-1/2 x 9-1/2

102210	Large Flat	can $7.95 | **US $4.95**
102757	Medium Flat	can $7.25 | **US $4.50**
103104	Small Flat	can $6.50 | **US $3.95**
101028	Large Gusset	can $10.50 | **US $6.50**
100664	Medium Gusset	can $8.50 | **US $5.25**

i. Organdy Bags (3 per package) Heat emboss these delicate bags for beautiful effects. Use caution, as bags will melt with extreme heat. Large: 5-3/4 x 14; Medium: 5-3/4 x 9; Small: 3-3/4 x 6.

102306	Large	can $7.95 | **US $4.95**
100993	Medium	can $6.50 | **US $3.95**
101623	Small	can $4.95 | **US $2.95**

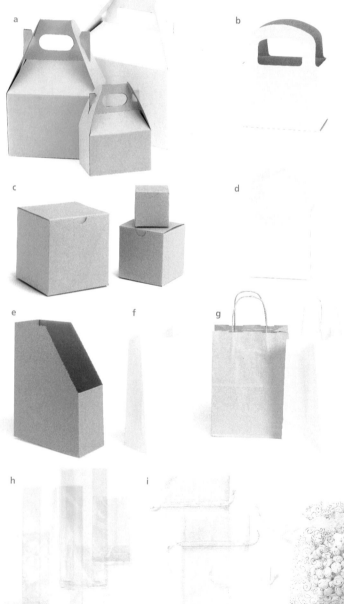

punches

Shape Punches

103375	1-3/8" Square *new!*	can $22.95 | **US $13.95**
103219	1-1/4" Circle	can $17.95 | **US $10.95**
102903	Maple Leaf	can $17.95 | **US $10.95**
102836	Oak Leaf	can $17.95 | **US $10.95**
101694	Daisy	can $15.95 | **US $9.95**
100708	Dragonfly	can $15.95 | **US $9.95**
102826	Small Snowflake	can $7.95 | **US $4.95**
103377	Folk Heart *new!*	can $15.95 | **US $9.95**
103376	Folk Star *new!*	can $15.95 | **US $9.95**

Corner Pocket Punches

102439	Heart Pocket	can $17.95 | **US $10.95**
102806	Star Pocket	can $17.95 | **US $10.95**
103381	Square Steps Pocket *new!*	can $17.95 | **US $10.95**

Corner Slot Punches

102140	ZigZag Slot	can $17.95 | **US $10.95**
102881	Ribbon Slot	can $17.95 | **US $10.95**
103380	Wrought Iron Slot *new!*	can $17.95 | **US $10.95**

Corner Punches

102504	Lace Corner	can $16.50 | **US $9.95**
101032	Deco Corner	can $16.50 | **US $9.95**
103255	Southwest Corner	can $16.50 | **US $9.95**
103378	Small Corner Rounder *new!*	can $9.95 | **US $5.95**
103379	Large Corner Rounder *new!*	can $17.95 | **US $10.95**

Hand-Held Punches

101227	1/16" Circle	can $14.50 | **US $8.95**
100391	1/8" Circle *new!*	can $14.50 | **US $8.95**
100392	1/4" Circle *new!*	can $14.50 | **US $8.95**
102686	Rectangle	can $14.50 | **US $8.95**

Please note: To keep up with the high demand for our punches, Stampin' Up!® may order punches from more than one supplier to avoid backorders. Therefore, the designs shown here may vary slightly.

tip

Use the small corner rounder and the large corner rounder together to create perfect mats!

1-3/8" square

1-1/4" circle

maple leaf

oak leaf

daisy

dragonfly   small snowflake   folk heart   folk star

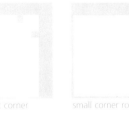

heart pocket   star pocket   square steps pocket

zigzag slot   ribbon slot   wrought iron slot

lace corner   deco corner   southwest corner   small corner rounder   large corner rounder

1/16" circle   1/8" circle   1/4" circle   Rectangle

adhesives

a. 2-Way Glue Pen This adhesive is temporary when allowed to dry before adhering, or permanent when adhered promptly.

100425   2-Way Glue Pen   can $4.95 | **US $2.95**

b. Liquid Glue Dual-tipped applicator lets you apply this clear, gel-like glue in thin lines or over wide areas. Acid free. (24 ml.)

102620   Liquid Glue   can $6.50 | **US $3.95**

c. HERMAfix® Vario Tabs 1,000 adhesive tabs in a convenient dispenser. Acid free.

102956   HERMAfix Vario Tabs   can $24.95 | **US $14.95**

103115   HERMAfix Vario Tabs Refill   can $12.50 | **US $7.50**

d. HERMAfix® Transfer Tiny adhesive dots in a convenient dispenser. (585 inches) Acid free.

103305   HERMAfix Transfer   can $19.95 | **US $11.95**

100902   HERMAfix Transfer Refill   can $10.95 | **US $6.50**

e. Clear Fix Transparent Mounting Squares (500) Acid free.

100481   Clear Fix Transparent Mounting Squares   can $7.95 | **US $4.95**

f. Glue Stick (3 per package) Goes on purple and dries clear.

102463   Glue Stick   can $7.25 | **US $4.50**

g. Heat & Stick Powder This product lets you apply glitter or flocking to your entire stamped image with precision. Acid free. (1/2 oz.)

100625   Heat & Stick Powder   can $7.25 | **US $4.50**

h. Permanent Mono® Adhesive Double-stick adhesive in a convenient dispenser (472 inches) Acid free. *new design!*

103383   Permanent Mono Adhesive   can $10.95 | **US $6.95**

103382   Permanent Mono Adhesive Refill   can $6.95 | **US $4.25**

i. Stampin' Dimensionals™ 100 each of 1/8-inch thick and 1/16-inch thick double-sided, adhesive foam dots. Acid free.

100476   Stampin' Dimensionals   can $5.95 | **US $3.50**

storage

j. Cropper Hopper™ Supply Tote This sturdy case provides a convenient way to carry all your favorite accessories. With tools on one side and stamps and paper on the other, stamping becomes a go-anywhere hobby. Manufactured exclusively for Stampin' Up!® 11-1/2 x 10-3/4 x 4.

103207   Cropper Hopper Supply Tote   can $23.95 | **US $14.95**

k. Craft Keepers Safe storage for photos, papers, card stock, templates, and more. Velcro® closure. Expands to one inch thick. (3 per package)

101832   12 x 12   can $12.95 | **US $7.95**

102459   8-1/2 x 11   can $11.95 | **US $6.95**

scissors & cutters

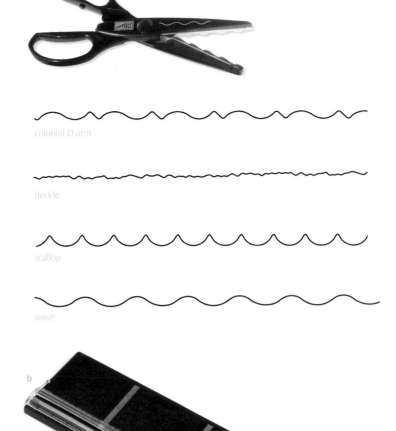

a. Decorative Edge Scissors These large-handled scissors allow ease in cutting and come in 4 great patterns! 3-inch blade length.

102303	Colonial Charm	can $11.95 | **US $6.95**
101053	Deckle	can $11.95 | **US $6.95**
101130	Scallop	can $11.95 | **US $6.95**
100610	Wave	can $11.95 | **US $6.95**

colonial charm

deckle

scallop

wave

b. Paper Cutter Cuts paper up to 12 inches wide. Comes with 2 cutting blades. Refills come with either a cutting and scoring blade or two cutting blades.

102587	Paper Cutter	can $34.95 | **US $21.95**
101285	Cutting & Scoring Blade Refills	can $7.95 | **US $4.95**
100955	Cutting Blade Refills	can $7.95 | **US $4.95**

c. Craft & Rubber Scissors These sharp, short-bladed scissors are great for multipurpose use and are especially suited for trimming your rubber stamps before mounting them.

| 103179 | Craft & Rubber Scissors | can $32.95 \| **US $19.95** |

d. The Tearing Edge Create natural-looking torn edges with precision.

| 102930 | The Tearing Edge | can $31.95 \| **US $19.95** |

e. Acrylic Graph with Grid Large, easy-to-read numbers in two directions eliminate the need to turn the ruler. The computer-generated grid ensures accurate and consistent cuts with your hobby blade. (6 x 12)

| 103158 | Acrylic Graph with Grid | can $15.95 \| **US $9.95** |

f. Cutting Mat This no-slip mat allows for safe cutting while protecting desks, tables, and countertops. Grid lines provide a guide for perfect cutting with your hobby blade every time. The self-healing mat means that no cut marks affect your next cut. (12 x 18)

| 101087 | Cutting Mat | can $23.95 \| **US $14.95** |

g. Hobby Blade & Refills Extra sharp, with 5 refill blades. Comes in a convenient storage tube.

| 102449 | Hobby Blade & Refills | can $7.25 \| **US $4.50** |

tip For best results, put The Tearing Edge on the paper, press it down with your hand, and pull the paper slowly toward you. Use the bottom edge for a rougher tear and the top edge for a finer tear.

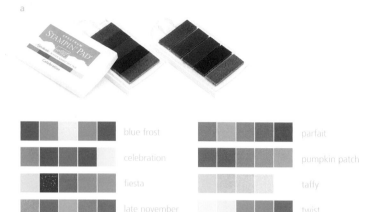

a

blue frost
celebration
fiesta
late november

parfait
pumpkin patch
taffy
twist

b

c

d

gold
silver

e

azure
blazing red
forest green
jet black
mustard

olive green
pumpkin
royal purple
timber brown
ultramarine

ink pads

a. Stampin' Up!® Spectrum Pads Selections from our exclusive 48 colors arranged in fabulous spectrums! These multicolor pads use the same acid free dye inks as our Classic Stampin' Pads®, so your Classic Stampin' Ink® refills will re-ink both pads. (Specific colors used are listed on each Spectrum pad for easy refilling.) The innovative and easy-to-use pad design prevents the inks from bleeding during storage.

Spectrum pads are a quick and easy way to give a burst of color to any image. You can also create eye-catching rainbow backgrounds with a Spectrum pad and a rubber brayer.

102694	Blue Frost	CAN $18.95 I **US $11.95**
101492	Celebration	CAN $18.95 I **US $11.95**
101207	Fiesta	CAN $18.95 I **US $11.95**
102367	Late November	CAN $18.95 I **US $11.95**
102073	Parfait	CAN $18.95 I **US $11.95**
101336	Pumpkin Patch	CAN $18.95 I **US $11.95**
103238	Taffy	CAN $18.95 I **US $11.95**
100926	Twist	CAN $18.95 I **US $11.95**

Create your own color combination with our Classic Ink Refills!

| 100000 | Empty Spectrum Pad *new!* | CAN $14.50 I **US $8.95** |

b. VersaMark® Create a tone-on-tone design or a watermark effect with this unique pad and marker. Acid free. Nontoxic. Refill is 1/2 oz.

102283	VersaMark Pad	CAN $12.50 I **US $7.50**
102193	VersaMark Pad Ink Refill	CAN $5.95 I **US $3.75**
100901	VersaMarker™	CAN $5.50 I **US $3.25**

c. Top Boss® Tinted Embossing Pad Refill is 1/2 oz.

| 101248 | Top Boss Tinted Embossing Pad | CAN $9.95 I **US $6.25** |
| 103137 | Top Boss Tinted Embossing Pad Refill | CAN $6.50 I **US $3.95** |

d. Encore!® Ultimate Metallic Pads Add a rich, metallic look to your stamped projects with these acid-free, fade-resistant pigment ink pads. Metallic inks should be heat embossed when used in a scrapbook. These inks come in stackable, easy-to-hold pads. Refills are 1/2 oz.

101017	Gold	CAN $14.95 I **US $8.95**
101242	Gold Refill	CAN $6.95 I **US $4.25**
101039	Silver	CAN $14.95 I **US $8.95**
102124	Silver Refill	CAN $6.95 I **US $4.25**

e. StazOn™ Ink Pads This quick-drying, permanent ink works great on plastic and porcelain. Refills are 1/2 oz.

	StazOn Pad CAN $12.95 **US $7.95**	StazOn Refill CAN $7.95 **US $4.95**	
Azure *new!*	103359	103356	-
Blazing Red	103000	101234	-
Forest Green *new!*	103360	103357	-
Jet Black	101406	102566	-
Mustard	101987	102850	-
Olive Green	102079	101438	-
Pumpkin *new!*	103358	103355	-
Royal Purple *new!*	103353	103354	-
Timber Brown	103088	100945	-
Ultramarine	103146	102378	-

tip

Use our exclusive Watercolor Pencils wet or dry to create a unique look. When they're dry they work like colored pencils and are great for coloring line images or sprucing up backgrounds. Scribble onto a scratch paper, blend the color with a dampened brush or a blender pen then color your image for a watercolor effect on any project. You can also color your image and blend the color with a dampened brush or a blender pen.

pencils & markers

a. Watercolor Pencils 24 assorted colors. Made with deep pigments, our brilliantly colored pencils come in a sturdy tin container. Use alone to color stamped images or use with a blender pen or dampened watercolor brush for lovely watercolor effects. Acid free.

101879   Watercolor Pencils   can $32.95 | **US $19.95**

b. Metallic Color Pencils Add a rich metallic luster to your stamped images. Convenient storage tube included. 12 assorted colors.

101120   Metallic Color Pencils   can $32.95 | **US $19.95**

c. Pure Color Pencils *new!* You'll love these new pure color pencils! Color goes on smooth. Color runs throughout the no-wood pencil, but it can be sharpened just like a regular pencil. Thin black coating can be scraped away. 12 assorted colors. (Black, Rust, Brown, Spring Green, Green, Blue, Periwinkle, Purple, Pink, Red, Orange, Yellow)

100271   Pure Color Pencils   can $32.95 | **US $19.95**

d. Pencil Sharpener Sharp steel blade gives a fine point every time. Two sizes accommodate a range of pencils. Removable receptacle for shavings keeps things neat.

100745   Pencil Sharpener   can $7.95 | **US $4.95**

e. Fabrico® Markers Pigment ink markers for the archival-conscious scrapbooker. Also great for fabrics and crafts. Specially packaged for Stampin' Up! in color groups that coordinate with our exclusive 48 colors. (6 per package)

103078   Brights   can $30.95 | **US $18.95**
100968   Earths/Regals   can $30.95 | **US $18.95**
101729   Pastels   can $30.95 | **US $18.95**

f. Zig® Painty Double-tipped opaque pen.

102673   Gold/Silver   can $9.95 | **US $5.95**

g. Blender Pens (3 per package) 2 brush tips on each. Use with Watercolor Pencils and Stampin' Pastels® to blend color.

102845   Blender Pens   can $16.50 | **US $9.95**

h. Watercolor Brushes

101331   Small   can $9.50 | **US $5.95**
101551   Medium   can $10.95 | **US $6.95**
100894   Large Flat   can $17.95 | **US $10.95**

brights
earths/regals
pastels

can't do without it!

a. Stampin' Scrub™ Clean-Up Pad Get efficient, easy cleaning with this dual-sided tray containing replaceable black fiber scrubbing pads. Clean stamp on one side, blot dry on the other. Sized to fit even our largest stamps. Another Stampin' Up!® exclusive! Each pad is 7-1/2 x 4-5/8. Refills come in pkg. of 2.

102642	Stampin' Scrub Clean-Up Pad	can $23.95 | **US $14.95**
101230	Stampin' Scrub Clean-Up Refill Pads	can $12.95 | **US $7.95**

b. Stampin' Mist® Stamp Cleaner Light rose-scented spray cleans and conditions your rubber stamps. (2 oz.) Refill (8 oz.)

102394	Stampin' Mist	can $6.50 | **US $3.95**
101022	Stampin' Mist Refill	can $14.50 | **US $8.95**

c. Stampin' Up! Grid Paper Oversized pad of paper protects your stamping work surfaces. Serves as scratch paper and makes cleanup a snap! Printed on one side with a grid and ruler for convenient measurements. 11 x 17. (100 sheets)

102787	Stampin' Up! Grid Paper	can $15.95 | **US $9.95**

d. Stamping Sponges (3 per package)

101610	Stamping Sponges	can $5.95 | **US $3.50**

e. Sponge Daubers (12 per package)

102892	Sponge Daubers	can $16.50 | **US $9.95**

f. Inkworx® Air Art Tool Achieve spectacular air-brushed effects using a marker and this tool. Great for use with stencils and for backgrounds. (Marker not included.)

101015	Inkworx Air Art Tool	can $12.95 | **US $7.95**

g. Bone Folder Use to score paper and make crisp folds.

102300	Bone Folder	can $10.95 | **US $6.50**

h. Stamp-a-ma-jig™ Use this stamp positioner for fast and precise stamp alignment every time. Nonskid base. Includes reusable, wipe-clean placement sheet. (Stamp shown not included.)

101049	Stamp-a-ma-jig	can $19.95 | **US $11.95**

i. Brayers For special-effects backgrounds and uniform inking on large stamps, nothing beats a brayer. Includes handle and soft rubber snap-in cylinder. Acrylic and Foam Snap-Ins fit in the brayer handle shown and are sold separately.

102395	Rubber Brayer & Handle	can $18.95 | **US $11.50**
100430	Acrylic Snap-In Brayer	can $11.95 | **US $7.50**
101052	Foam Snap-In Brayer	can $10.95 | **US $6.95**

j. Paper Crimper Crimps paper up to 6-1/2 inches wide.

101618	Paper Crimper	can $32.95 | **US $19.95**

color it!

a. Stampin' Kids® Pads These recessed pads are designed with kids in mind. The ink is bright and washes off hands and out of most clothing (may require repeat washing). Pad surface: 1-7/8 x 2-3/4

101577	Bear Brown	can $4.95 | **US $2.95**
100799	Beetle Black	can $4.95 | **US $2.95**
103203	Boxcar Blue	can $4.95 | **US $2.95**
101887	Gumball Green	can $4.95 | **US $2.95**
102453	Poppin' Purple	can $4.95 | **US $2.95**
101897	Princess Pink	can $4.95 | **US $2.95**
101177	Robin Red	can $4.95 | **US $2.95**
102588	Yahoo Yellow	can $4.95 | **US $2.95**

b. Stampin' Kids® Markers Fun and economical way to introduce kids to the fun of paper arts. As with any child's art project, cover child's clothing for protection. 20 assorted colors.

102328   Stampin' Kids Markers   can $7.95 \| **US $4.95**

c. Art Pencils (12 per package) Acid free.

101092   Art Pencils   can $11.95 \| **US $6.95**

a

bear brown
beetle black
boxcar blue
gumball green
poppin' purple
princess pink
robin red
yahoo yellow

b

c

wear it!

Kids of all ages love our Tattoo Kits! Nontoxic, FD&C-approved inks fade and wash off within about a day. Stamps are shown actual size.

d. Tattoo Kit I Contents: Black pad, 6 markers (Yellow, Henna, Black, Red, Green, Blue) and 6 stamps in a vinyl pouch.

100388	Tattoo Kit I *new!*	can $22.95 | **US $13.95**
101982	Black Tattoo Ink Refill (1/2 oz.)	can $6.50 | **US $3.95**

e. Tattoo Kit II Contents: Navy pad, 6 markers (Blue, Pink, Purple, Orange, Red, Green) and 6 stamps in a vinyl pouch.

100389	Tattoo Kit II *new!*	can $22.95 | **US $13.95**
101562	Navy Tattoo Ink Refill (1/2 oz.)	can $6.50 | **US $3.95**

f. Tattoo Markers *new!* (6 per package) Blue, Orange, Black, Green, Pink, Purple. Nontoxic, acid free. Dries quickly, washes off easily.

100390   Tattoo Markers   can $10.95 \| **US $6.95**

d

e

f

tattoo kit I

tattoo kit II

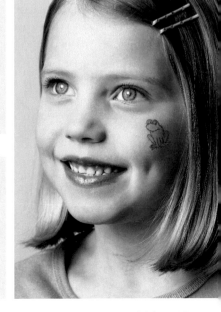

a

b

c

d

e

black
opaque and bold

classy copper
copper with a rich shine

crystal clear
smooth-flowing, clear powder to be used over
colored ink, allowing the color to show through

gold glory
gold metallic with a foil-like shine

hologram highlights
crystal clear base with hologram glitter
for a reflective flashy shine

iridescent ice
crystal clear base with iridescent glitter
for stunning sparkle

sterling silver
silver metallic with a foil-like shine

vintage verdigris
green with copper patina

winter white
crisp, opaque white

f

black

clear

gold

silver

white

g

brights
red, green, orange, pink

earth tones
mustard, olive, rust, dark brown

regal tones
burgundy, forest green, blue, navy

subtles
light blue, light pink, lavender, sage

heat embossing

a. Embossing Heat Tool *new design!* Use this electric heat tool with embossing powders, Liquid Applique™ and to heat-set pigment inks.

100005 Embossing Heat Tool can $42.95 I **US $26.95**

b. Powder Pals Keep your work area neat and save glitters and powders with this terrific tool. Comes with 2 trays and a brush to help in cleanup.

102197 Powder Pals can $31.95 I **US $19.95**

c. Embossing Buddy Rub across paper to reduce static.

103083 Embossing Buddy can $7.25 I **US $4.50**

d. Embossing Kit Contents: 1/2 oz. Sterling Silver Stampin' Emboss® Powder, 1/2 oz. Gold Glory Stampin' Emboss Powder, Mini Top Boss® Tinted Embossing Pad, 1/2 oz. Top Boss Tinted Embossing Refill, and instructions for use.

103280 Embossing Kit can $23.95 I **US $14.95**

e. Stampin' Emboss Powder Add dimension and impact to any image. Try them on your next masterpiece! All powders are acid free.

102440	Black (1 oz.)	can $7.25 I **US $4.50**
100442	Classy Copper (1 oz.)	can $7.25 I **US $4.50**
101058	Crystal Clear (1 oz.)	can $7.25 I **US $4.50**
101419	Crystal Clear (4 oz.)	can $20.95 I **US $12.95**
100837	Gold Glory (1 oz.)	can $7.25 I **US $4.50**
102526	Gold Glory (4 oz.)	can $20.95 I **US $12.95**
103151	Hologram Highlights (1 oz.)	can $7.25 I **US $4.50**
101930	Iridescent Ice (1/2 oz.)	can $7.25 I **US $4.50**
103273	Sterling Silver (1 oz.)	can $7.25 I **US $4.50**
100526	Vintage Verdigris (1 oz.)	can $7.25 I **US $4.50**
100551	Winter White (1 oz.)	can $7.25 I **US $4.50**

Enamel Embossing Powder Give a higher loft to your embossing and achieve incredible stained-glass effects with this ultrathick embossing powder. (1 oz.)

100477 Glassy Glaze can $7.25 I **US $4.50**

f. Detail Embossing Powder This powder preserves the fine detail in your stamped images. 1/2 oz.

101040	Black	can $7.25 I **US $4.50**
101428	Clear	can $7.25 I **US $4.50**
103342	Gold	can $7.25 I **US $4.50**
101781	Silver	can $7.25 I **US $4.50**
100963	White	can $7.25 I **US $4.50**

g. Embossing Stacks *new!* With stacks, it's easy to coordinate colors. 4 stacks available with 1/2 oz. each of 4 colors.

100091	Brights	can $26.95 I **US $16.95**
100089	Earth Tones	can $26.95 I **US $16.95**
100090	Regal Tones	can $26.95 I **US $16.95**
100088	Subtles	can $26.95 I **US $16.95**

tip We recommend the VersaMark® or Top Boss® embossing pads (sold on page 224) for your embossing projects.

dry embossing

Classy Brass™ Templates All Classy Brass templates feature exclusive designs that coordinate with popular Stampin' Up!® stamp sets. Most templates also feature a decorative edge for embossed borders. For the custom look of elegant embossed images combined with coordinating stamped images, collect all of these beautiful designs and companion stamp sets.

102986	All-Around Alphabet	can $23.95 | **US $14.95**
100399	Bold Basics *new!*	can $23.95 | **US $14.95**
102273	Bold Greetings	can $23.95 | **US $14.95**
100919	Butterflies	can $15.95 | **US $9.95**
100496	Daisy	can $23.95 | **US $14.95**
100403	Delightful Doodles *new!*	can $15.95 | **US $9.95**
103291	Fancy Flowers	can $15.95 | **US $9.95**
102865	Festive Fall	can $23.95 | **US $14.95**
101665	Frames & Borders	can $23.95 | **US $14.95**
100842	Fresh Flowers	can $23.95 | **US $14.95**
102688	Little Shapes	can $23.95 | **US $14.95**
100402	Love without End *new!*	can $23.95 | **US $14.95**
100401	Simply Spring *new!*	can $23.95 | **US $14.95**
100400	Snowflakes *new!*	can $23.95 | **US $14.95**
102270	Special Occasion	can $23.95 | **US $14.95**
101963	Squares & Minis	can $15.95 | **US $9.95**

a. Light Table Embossing has never been easier! Our light table gives you the perfect large, flat surface for use with our Classy Brass templates.
(10 x 12 work area)

102888   Light Table   can $79.95 \| **US $49.95**

b. Stylus Tool Use small tip for lightweight papers and large tip for card stock.

100663   Stylus Tool   can $4.25 \| **US $2.50**

c. Empressor™ Stylus Dual-tipped, roller-ball embossing tool works with any template. Smooth-rolling action reduces paper tearing. Small tip is perfect for small patterns and lightweight papers; large tip works great on card stock.

100716   Empressor Stylus   can $17.95 \| **US $10.95**

all-around alphabet

bold basics

bold greetings

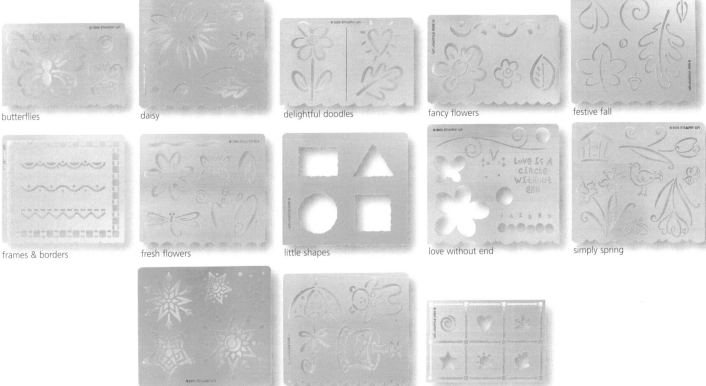

butterflies

daisy

delightful doodles

fancy flowers

festive fall

frames & borders

fresh flowers

little shapes

love without end

simply spring

snowflakes

special occasion

squares & minis

lumiere-pearlescent white

aztec gold

blue russet

bright yellow

micro pearl

duo blue/green

misty lavender

duo green/yellow

silver

duo red/blue

spring green

interference blue

super bronze

interference gold

super copper

interference green

super russet

interference red

true blue

interference violet

turquoise

The top swatch represents each color applied to black paper,
and the larger bottom swatch is applied to white paper.

pearl ex powders

a. Pearl Ex Achieve fabulous effects from a smooth, pearly luster to a highly metallic sheen with these versatile iridescent powders! Mix with Lumiere® liquid medium to apply as a paint, or apply dry with a watercolor or stipple brush or sponge. Mix with embossing powder for shimmery embossing.

101319	Lumiere-Pearlescent White	can $9.50 | **US $5.95**
101776	Aztec Gold	can $9.50 | **US $5.95**
103169	Blue Russet	can $9.50 | **US $5.95**
100002	Bright Yellow *new!*	can $9.50 | **US $5.95**
101195	Duo Blue/Green	can $9.50 | **US $5.95**
102474	Duo Green/Yellow	can $9.50 | **US $5.95**
102844	Duo Red/Blue	can $9.50 | **US $5.95**
101925	Interference Blue	can $9.50 | **US $5.95**
102345	Interference Gold	can $9.50 | **US $5.95**
101865	Interference Green	can $9.50 | **US $5.95**
100635	Interference Red	can $9.50 | **US $5.95**
103303	Interference Violet	can $9.50 | **US $5.95**
100004	Micro Pearl *new!*	can $9.50 | **US $5.95**
100643	Misty Lavender	can $9.50 | **US $5.95**
100003	Silver *new!*	can $9.50 | **US $5.95**
100509	Spring Green	can $9.50 | **US $5.95**
103021	Super Bronze	can $9.50 | **US $5.95**
102479	Super Copper	can $9.50 | **US $5.95**
101093	Super Russet	can $9.50 | **US $5.95**
101797	True Blue	can $9.50 | **US $5.95**
102248	Turquoise	can $9.50 | **US $5.95**

b. Stipple Brushes (2 per package) No. 2 and No. 4

101399	Stipple Brushes	can $11.95 | **US $6.95**

glitter

a. Glitter Stacks Stacks offer fabulous color selections for every purpose. A spot of sparkle transforms your creations! Apply with Heat & Stick Powder, Liquid Glue, or a 2-Way Glue Pen, sold separately. Each stack contains five 1/2 oz. bottles.

101851	Enchanted	can $33.95 | **US $20.95**
101303	Neon Lights	can $33.95 | **US $20.95**
100782	Pastel Diamonds	can $33.95 | **US $20.95**

b. Glitter Singles (1/2 oz.) *new!*

102023	Dazzling Diamonds	can $7.25 | **US $4.50**
103351	Gold Glitz	can $7.25 | **US $4.50**
103350	Green Glimmer	can $7.25 | **US $4.50**
103352	Romantic Red	can $7.25 | **US $4.50**
103349	Silver Shine	can $7.25 | **US $4.50**

Heat & Stick Powder is an excellent product for adhering glitter and Pearl Ex to your stamped image. See page 222 for ordering information.

texture it!

c. Crystal Effects Add a dimensional, lacquered look to any stamped image. (2 oz.) Acid free.

101055	Crystal Effects	can $10.25 | **US $6.25**

d. Liquid Appliqué Apply and heat for fluffy, dimensional look. Acid free.

101626	White	can $4.95 | **US $2.95**

e. Stampin' Flock Add a soft, fuzzy, touchable texture. For complete and easy coverage, use with Heat & Stick Powder.

101544	Bearly Brown	can $4.95 | **US $2.95**
102827	Whisper White	can $4.95 | **US $2.95**

enchanted

Blue Brilliance   Rose Ritz   Lavender Lights   Seafoam Splendor   Fabulous Fuchsia

neon lights

Electric Yellow   Radical Blue   Vivid Pink   Shocking Punch   Wet Lime

pastel diamonds

Coral Crystal   Periwinkle Blue   Sun Sparkle   Razzle Berry   Mystic Mint

dazzling diamonds   gold glitz   green glimmer

romantic red   silver shine

Add a spot of shine to your stamped images with Crystal Effects. For an overall gloss, brush Crystal Effects over the entire surface of your card stock or paper with a watercolor brush.

a. Skeleton Leaves Add these beautiful, eye-catching accents to almost any project for a touch of nature or simply something different. Apply directly to projects, or use as stencils with a brayer. All natural—colors and shapes may vary. (10 per package)

102750 Skeleton Leaves   can $7.95 | **US $4.95**

b. Mini Deco Fasteners Wonderful for embellishing and layering. Can be embossed for a variety of colors! Use a 1/16-inch circle punch to make holes for these tiny fasteners. (approx. 100 per package)

103147 Gold   can $6.50 | **US $3.95**
102823 Silver   can $6.50 | **US $3.95**

c. Wire Works Wonderful wire for whimsical accents! Available in 2 weights: choose 22-gauge for a slightly thicker and heavier wire and 26-gauge when you want a thinner, more flexible wire. Acid free.

12 colors, approx. 8 yards per spool. (Seafoam Green, Red, Green, Magenta, Purple, Forest, Dark Blue, Silver, Lemon, Plum, Tangerine, Gold)
102808 26-Gauge   can $31.95 | **US $19.95**

12 colors, approx. 6 yards per spool. (Tangerine, Peach, Dark Blue, Magenta, Natural, Red, Purple, Silver, Lemon, Green, Christmas Green, Peacock Blue)
101833 22-Gauge   can $31.95 | **US $19.95**

d. Write Me a Memory Journaling Fonts CD Contains exclusive fonts offering the ease and flexibility of computer journaling while providing the handwritten look that makes each page feel unique and personal. English only | En aglais seulement

System Requirements: PC—Windows 95 or higher, Pentium/equivalent or higher. Macintosh—Macintosh Power PC Processor, System 8.5 or higher.

100482 Write Me a Memory Journaling Fonts CD   can $23.95 | **US $14.95**

Embellish your projects with the hottest new accessory around! Colors coordinate with many of our 48 colors. Eyelet tools sold separately.

new design! Each container comes with approx. 200 eyelets. Assortments come with approx. 50 each of 4 colors. Refer to pages 208-209 for color swatches.

100370	Black	can $9.50	**US $5.95**
100374	Gold	can $9.50	**US $5.95**
100372	Real Red	can $9.50	**US $5.95**
100373	Silver	can $9.50	**US $5.95**
100371	White	can $9.50	**US $5.95**

Basic: Black, White, Gold, Silver
100377 Basic Assortment   can $9.50 | **US $5.95**

Bold Brights I: Brilliant Blue, Yoyo Yellow, Real Red, Glorious Green
100375 Bold Brights I Assortment   can $9.50 | **US $5.95**

Bold Brights II: Green Galore, Lovely Lilac, Only Orange, Positively Pink
100376 Bold Brights II Assortment   can $9.50 | **US $5.95**

Earth Elements: Old Olive, More Mustard, Really Rust, Creamy Caramel
100381 Earth Elements Assortment   can $9.50 | **US $5.95**

Rich Regals: Night of Navy, Baroque Burgundy, Forest Foliage, Bordering Blue
100380 Rich Regals Assortment   can $9.50 | **US $5.95**

Soft Subtles I: Pretty in Pink, Barely Banana, Mellow Moss, Perfect Plum
100378 Soft Subtles I Assortment   can $9.50 | **US $5.95**

Soft Subtles II: Sage Shadow, Blush Blossom, Lavender Lace, Bliss Blue
100379 Soft Subtles II Assortment   can $9.50 | **US $5.95**

new! Each container comes with approx. 200 eyelets, approx. 50 each of 4 colors.

Large Circles: White, Silver, Real Red, Black
100367 Large Circles   can $15.95 | **US $9.95**

Large Ovals: Perfect Plum, Old Olive, Baroque Burgundy, Vanilla
100365 Large Ovals   can $15.95 | **US $9.95**

Large Hearts: Real Red, Pretty in Pink, White, Pink Passion
100366 Large Hearts   can $15.95 | **US $9.95**

Large Flowers: Real Red, Yoyo Yellow, Positively Pink, Lovely Lilac
100368 Large Flowers   can $15.95 | **US $9.95**

Small Flowers: Pretty in Pink, White, Lavender Lace, Barely Banana
100369 Small Flowers   can $15.95 | **US $9.95**

Brocade Blue, More Mustard, Close to Cocoa, Ruby Red
100364 Squares   can $15.95 | **US $9.95**

Stars: Real Red, Summer Sun, Brilliant Blue, Silver
100362 Stars   can $15.95 | **US $9.95**

Triangles: Tempting Turquoise, Silver, Only Orange, Green Galore
100363 Triangles   can $15.95 | **US $9.95**

new! Contains 1/4-inch anywhere punch (great for setting larger eyelets), mini hammer, and tweezers.
103733 Companion Eyelet Tool Kit   can $31.95 | **US $19.95**

Includes 1/8-inch anywhere punch and eyelet setter.
101016 Eyelet Tool Kit   can $12.95 | **US $7.95**

a. Grosgrain Ribbon (1/4-inch wide; Red-White-&-Blue is 3/8-inch wide) approx. 25 yards. Listed in the order pictured.

101926	Light Pink	can $9.95 | **US $5.95**
103064	Tangerine	can $9.95 | **US $5.95**
102684	Yellow Gold	can $9.95 | **US $5.95**
101298	Maize	can $9.95 | **US $5.95**
100455	Cream	can $9.95 | **US $5.95**
102819	White	can $9.95 | **US $5.95**
102712	Black	can $9.95 | **US $5.95**
100538	Bluebird	can $9.95 | **US $5.95**
103113	Delphinium	can $9.95 | **US $5.95**
101666	Light Orchid	can $9.95 | **US $5.95**
102718	Cranberry	can $9.95 | **US $5.95**
102682	Red	can $9.95 | **US $5.95**
101569	Rose	can $9.95 | **US $5.95**
100001	Kelly Green *new!*	can $9.95 | **US $5.95**
101637	Apple Green	can $9.95 | **US $5.95**
103114	Spring Moss	can $9.95 | **US $5.95**
101156	Taupe	can $9.95 | **US $5.95**
100847	Royal	can $9.95 | **US $5.95**
102119	Turquoise	can $9.95 | **US $5.95**
102950	French Blue	can $9.95 | **US $5.95**
101570	Red-White-&-Blue	can $10.95 | **US $6.25**

b. Wide Organdy Ribbon (7/8-inch wide) Approx. 25 yards. Listed in the order pictured.

103270	Silver	can $10.95 | **US $6.25**
103107	Gold	can $10.95 | **US $6.25**
102650	Maize	can $10.95 | **US $6.25**
100525	Ivory	can $10.95 | **US $6.25**
101454	Mauve	can $10.95 | **US $6.25**
100437	Burgundy	can $10.95 | **US $6.25**
101441	Rainbow	can $14.95 | **US $8.95**
102978	White	can $10.95 | **US $6.25**
102735	Light Pink	can $10.95 | **US $6.25**
103046	Bright Pink	can $10.95 | **US $6.25**
101224	Red	can $10.95 | **US $6.25**
101597	Lavender	can $10.95 | **US $6.25**
100936	Purple	can $10.95 | **US $6.25**
101204	Royal Blue	can $10.95 | **US $6.25**
101854	Hunter Green	can $10.95 | **US $6.25**
102388	Olive Green	can $10.95 | **US $6.25**
102153	Celery	can $10.95 | **US $6.25**
101547	Kelly Green	can $10.95 | **US $6.25**
103163	Light Blue	can $10.95 | **US $6.25**
103283	Navy	can $10.95 | **US $6.25**
103315	Black	can $10.95 | **US $6.25**

c. Narrow Organdy Ribbon (3/8-inch wide) Approx. 25 yards. Listed in the order pictured.

101613	White	can $8.50 | **US $4.95**
100589	Ivory	can $8.50 | **US $4.95**
102055	Peach	can $8.50 | **US $4.95**
103019	Light Pink	can $8.50 | **US $4.95**
101644	Orchid	can $8.50 | **US $4.95**
102217	Blue	can $8.50 | **US $4.95**
100807	Light Blue	can $8.50 | **US $4.95**
102758	Light Green	can $8.50 | **US $4.95**

Be sure to check out the *Stampin' Memories Idea Book & Catalog* for an expanded selection of scrapbooking accessories, including albums, Simply Scrappin'® kits, and frame stamp sets.

a. Hemp (approx. 12 yards) Listed in the order shown.

101259	Black	can $4.25 | **US $2.50**
101080	Green	can $4.25 | **US $2.50**
102859	Purple	can $4.25 | **US $2.50**
101949	Gold	can $4.25 | **US $2.50**
100982	Natural	can $4.25 | **US $2.50**
102875	Red	can $4.25 | **US $2.50**
101509	Blue	can $4.25 | **US $2.50**

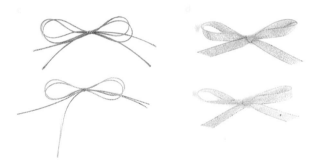

b. Raffia (2 oz.)

101957	Natural	can $9.50 | **US $5.95**

c. Metallic Cord (approx. 75 yards)

101299	Gold	can $9.95 | **US $5.95**
102492	Silver	can $9.95 | **US $5.95**

d. Metallic Ribbon 1/4-inch (approx. 25 yards)

101312	Gold	can $10.95 | **US $6.25**
100621	Silver	can $10.95 | **US $6.25**

e. Fancy Fibers *new!* You'll love our new fibers, which coordinate with our 48 colors. Add dimension to your cards, tags, and layouts. Make quick borders, frames, or accents. 6 colors on a card, approx. 2 yards of each color, approx. 12 yards total. Available in 5 different coordinating packages. Please purchase sufficient fibers to complete your project. Assortment may vary.

100395	Brights	can $11.50 | **US $6.95**
100396	Earth Tones	can $11.50 | **US $6.95**
100393	Regal Tones	can $11.50 | **US $6.95**
100394	Subtles	can $11.50 | **US $6.95**
100397	Neutrals	can $11.50 | **US $6.95**

brights   earth tones   regal tones   subtles   neutrals

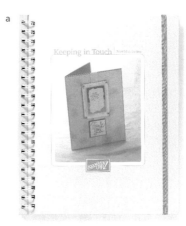

a

portfolio series

a. Keeping in Touch Stampin' Up!®'s admired Portfolio Series—idea books packed with creative and innovative ideas for stampers, scrapbookers, and crafters—takes a new turn! The latest Portfolio Series begins with a spiral-bound, hard cover book entitled *Keeping in Touch*. More than 100 pages feature full-color photos and step-by-step instructions on how to create over 40 fabulous greeting cards. Discover how handmade cards can enrich the lives of the people who make them as well as those who receive them. Projects range from cards you can produce in a snap to masterpieces that take more time—so both beginning and advanced stampers will find inspiring ideas. You'll want to create every card in this book, and we'll show you how, from start to finish.

100883 Keeping in Touch   can $39.95 | **US $24.95**

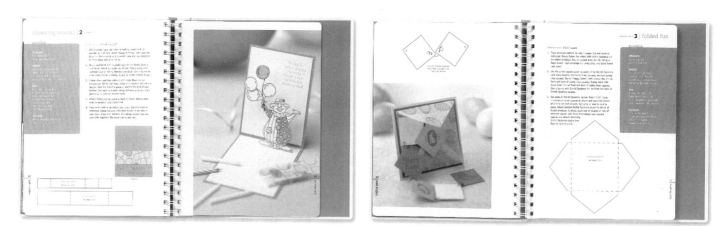

b

b. Gifts & Giving When the giving is as important as the gift, you're sure to find exactly what you're looking for in the newest addition to our Portfolio Series. *Gifts & Giving* features beautiful handmade gift ideas, as well as more than 50 fun and inspiring packaging ideas. Organized in Stampin' Up!'s exclusive four color families, you'll easily find the perfect idea for every gift-giving occasion.

100557 Gifts & Giving   can $39.95 | **US $24.95**

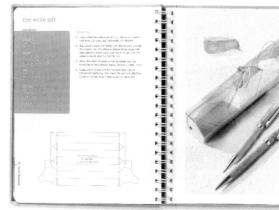

Cover A
Little Layers II, Crazy Alphabet, Classic Alphabet, and Classic Alphabet Numbers sets; Gable Green, Marvelous Magenta, Lovely Lilac, Ultrasmooth White, and Green Galore card stock; Green Galore, Marvelous Magenta, Lovely Lilac, and Lavender Lace Craft pads; watercolor brush; Silver eyelets; Sterling Silver embossing powder; Stampin' Dimensionals; 1/8" Circle punch; string; embroidery floss; needle

Cover B
Roses in Winter set; Lavender Lace, Gable Green, and Confetti White card stock; VersaMark pad; Lavender Lace and Lovely Lilac Classic pads; Marvelous Magenta Craft pad; watercolor brush; Scallop scissors; 1/8" Circle punch; Delphinium grosgrain ribbon; needle; bleach

Cover C
Roses in Winter and All-Year Cheer II sets; Gable Green card stock; Confetti White pouch box; Lovely Lilac, Lavender Lace, Gable Green, and Green Galore Classic pads; Lovely Lilac and Green Galore Craft pads; watercolor brush; Stampin' Dimensionals; vellum circle metal edge tag; Orchid narrow organdy ribbon; Purple hemp

Cover D
Seeds of Kindness and Classic Alphabet sets; By Definition background stamp; Lovely Lilac and Marvelous Magenta card stock; Confetti White tag sheet; VersaMark pad; Lovely Lilac and Marvelous Magenta Classic pads; Stampin' Pastels; watercolor brush; Sterling Silver embossing powder; Lovely Lilac large flower eyelets; Turquoise grosgrain ribbon; Stampin' Dimensional; stamping sponges; string; bleach

Cover E
Seeds of Kindness set; Radiant White vellum, Tempting Turquoise, Confetti White, and Lovely Lilac card stock; VersaMark pad; Tempting Turquoise and Lovely Lilac markers; air art tool; Stampin' Pastels; stamping sponges; Stampin' Dimensionals; Lovely Lilac and Bordering Blue eyelets; Orchid narrow organdy ribbon; sewing machine and thread; bleach

Cover F
Friendship's Journey set; French Script background stamp; Confetti White, Summer Sun, Marvelous Magenta, Lavender Lace, Lovely Lilac, and Tempting Turquoise card stock; Basic Black, Tempting Turquoise, Marvelous Magenta, and Lovely Lilac Classic pads; stamping sponges; Silver eyelets; watercolor brush; Stampin' Pastels; Silver Mini Deco Fasteners; Turquoise grosgrain ribbon; string; key charm

4-5 A
Hearts & Clovers and Simple Sayings II sets; Confetti White card stock; Mellow Moss favor box; Mellow Moss, Basic Black, Ruby Red, and Barely Banana Classic pads; watercolor brush; 1/16" Circle punch; Natural hemp

4-5 B
In the Wild and Fun Phrases sets; Bamboo II background stamp; Ultrasmooth White, Brocade Blue, and Mellow Moss card stock; Barely Banana pouch box; Barely Banana, Mellow Moss, and Brocade Blue Classic pads; watercolor brush; Stampin' Dimensionals; Barely Banana and Old Olive eyelets; Earth Tones fiber

4-5 C
Elegant Ornaments set; Antique background stamp; Bordering Blue, Ruby Red, and Ultrasmooth Vanilla card stock; Bordering Blue Classic pad; Stampin' Dimensionals; Cream grosgrain ribbon; Vanilla oval eyelets

4-5 D
Nice & Narrow set; Ruby Red, Barely Banana, Mellow Moss, and Confetti White card stock; Ruby Red Classic pad; VersaMark pad; Stampin' Pastels; watercolor brush; Cream grosgrain ribbon; Gold Mini Deco Fasteners; 1/16" Circle punch; Earth Tones fiber

4-5 E
I Like Your Style set; Swirls & Blossoms background stamp; Mellow Moss, Brocade Blue, Barely Banana, Confetti White, and Ruby Red card stock; Basic Black, Mellow Moss, Ruby Red, Brocade Blue, Bordering Blue, Old Olive, and Barely Banana Classic pads; watercolor brush; Mellow Moss, Bordering Blue, and Barely Banana eyelets; Spring Moss grosgrain ribbon; Stampin' Dimensionals; crochet thread; button; sewing machine and thread

6-7 A
Take Me Out to the Ballgame and Quirky Alphabet Upper sets; Not Quite Navy, Creamy Caramel, Ruby Red, and Old Olive card stock; Not Quite Navy and Ruby Red Craft pads; VersaMark pad; journaling marker; Stampin' Pastels; font CD; sewing machine and thread

6-7 B
Choo Choo, Classic Alphabet, and Bold Alphabet sets; Not Quite Navy, Old Olive, Ruby Red, Ultrasmooth White, and Radiant White vellum card stock; Ruby Red, Old Olive, Not Quite Navy, and Basic Black Craft pads; White eyelets; font CD

6-7 C
Classic Alphabet set; Toy Box Simply Scrappin' kit; Radiant White vellum card stock; Not Quite Navy and Old Olive Craft pads; font CD; embroidery floss; needle

8-9 A
Love without End set; Ballet Blue, Ultrasmooth White, and Rose Red card stock; Ballet Blue, Brilliant Blue, and Rose Red Classic pads; Bluebird grosgrain ribbon; 26-gauge Wire Works; needle

8-9 B
Love without End and Fresh Fillers sets; Rose Red, Ballet Blue, and Ultrasmooth White card stock; Brilliant Blue and Rose Red Classic pads; watercolor brush; Bluebird grosgrain ribbon; Stampin' Dimensionals; 1/8" Circle punch; string

8-9 C
Lovely Leaves and Many Thanks sets; Filigree background stamp; Ballet Blue and Confetti White card stock; Celery, Bright Pink, and Blue mulberry paper; Ballet Blue Classic pad; VersaMark pad; Sterling Silver embossing powder; Stampin' Pastels; Stampin' Dimensionals; 1/8" Circle punch; Regal Tones fiber; stamping sponges

8-9 D
Simple Sketches and Itty Bitty Backgrounds sets; Mint Melody, Confetti White, and Ballet Blue card stock; Ballet Blue, Brocade Blue, Mint Melody, and Sage Shadow Classic pads; VersaMark pad; Sterling Silver embossing powder; Stampin' Dimensionals; Silver metallic cord; Brocade Blue square eyelets; paper crimper

8-9 E
Roses in Winter and All-Year Cheer II sets; Rose Romance, Confetti White, and Mint Melody card stock; Rose Romance, Rose Red, Baroque Burgundy, Mint Melody, and Sage Shadow Classic pads; watercolor brush; Silver Mini Deco Fastener; Silver metallic cord

12-13 A
Sweet Treats and Fun Phrases sets; Whimsical Flowers wheel; Blush Blossom, Cameo Coral, Lavender Lace, and Confetti White card stock; Basic Black, Cameo Coral, Lavender Lace, More Mustard, and Old Olive Classic pads; watercolor brush; Blush Blossom eyelet; Peach narrow organdy ribbon; 1/8" Circle punch

12-13 B
Let's Party set; Party Fun wheel; Lavender Lace, Cameo Coral, and Ultrasmooth White card stock; Cameo Coral, Old Olive, and Lavender Lace Classic pads; Lavender Lace cartridge; VersaMark pad; Sterling Silver embossing powder; 1/16" Circle punch; 26-gauge Wire Works; Silver Mini Deco Fasteners; Stampin' Dimensionals

12-13 C
Sweet Treats and Birthday Greetings sets; Whimsical Flowers wheel; Cameo Coral, Lavender Lace, and Ultrasmooth White card stock; Lavender Lace Classic pad; Cameo Coral cartridge; VersaMark pad; Stampin' Pastels; Stampin' Dimensionals; 1/16" Circle punch; Light Orchid grosgrain ribbon; crochet thread

12-13 D
Let's Party set; Groovy Lines background stamp; Party Fun wheel; Eggplant Envy, Lavender Lace, Cameo Coral, and Ultrasmooth White card stock; Eggplant Envy and Cameo Coral Classic pads; Lavender Lace marker; Cameo Coral cartridge; 26-gauge Wire Works; 1/16" Circle punch; buttons

12-13 E
Etruscan and All-Year Cheer I sets; Etruscan Vine wheel; Old Olive, Eggplant Envy, and Confetti Cream card stock; Eggplant Envy Classic pad; Old Olive cartridge; VersaMark pad; Stampin' Pastels; Perfect Plum eyelets; Natural hemp; 1/8" Circle punch; stamping sponges

16 A
Teeny Tinies and Fun Phrases sets; Old Olive, Taken with Teal, More Mustard, and Baroque Burgundy card stock; Ultrasmooth Vanilla Circle AlphaAccents; Baroque Burgundy Classic pad; Jumbo Circle punch; Stampin' Dimensionals; needle; embroidery floss

16 B
Teeny Tinies set; Taken with Teal, More Mustard, Close to Cocoa, and Ultrasmooth Vanilla card stock; Chocolate Chip, Old Olive, Taken with Teal, Forest Foliage, and More Mustard Classic pads; Stampin' Dimensionals; White grosgrain ribbon (dyed with Old Olive Classic ink)

16 C
Close to Nature, Fresh Fillers, and All-Year Cheer II sets; Chocolate Chip, Old Olive, Really Rust, and Naturals Ivory card stock; Dark Brown mulberry paper; Basic Black, Chocolate Chip, Really Rust, Old Olive, Forest Foliage, and Taken with Teal Classic pads; stamping sponge; watercolor brush; Stampin' Dimensionals; Natural hemp

16 D
Close to Nature and All-Year Cheer I sets; Creamy Caramel, Old Olive, and Confetti White card stock; Basic Black, Close to Cocoa, Creamy Caramel, Old Olive, Forest Foliage, and More Mustard Classic pads; watercolor brush; Taupe grosgrain ribbon; Gold Mini Deco Fasteners; Classy Copper embossing powder; Stampin' Dimensionals; Natural hemp; needle; yarn; twig

16 E
Fresh Filler and Good Times sets; More Mustard, Baroque Burgundy, and Confetti White card stock; Confetti White tag sheet; Baroque Burgundy and More Mustard Classic pads; watercolor brush; Stampin' Dimensionals; Jumbo Square punch; 1/16" Circle punch; Red hemp

16 F
Fresh Fillers and All-Year Cheer I sets; Taken with Teal and Old Olive card stock; Confetti White tag sheet; Taken with Teal and Old Olive Classic pads; 1/8" Circle punch; Olive Green wide organdy ribbon; Stampin' Dimensionals; string

17 A
Simple Somethings and All-Year Cheer II sets; Taken with Teal, Ultrasmooth Vanilla, Old Olive, and Baroque Burgundy card stock; Taken with Teal Classic pad; Basic Black, Taken with Teal, Baroque Burgundy, and Old Olive markers; watercolor brush; Old Olive oval eyelet; Turquoise grosgrain ribbon (dyed with Taken with Teal Classic ink); Stampin' Dimensionals; Scallop scissors; Envelope Template Assortment II; string

17 B
Mostly Flowers and All-Year Cheer III sets; Baroque Burgundy, Creamy Caramel, Taken with Teal, and Ultrasmooth Vanilla card stock; Ultrasmooth Vanilla tag sheet; Chocolate Chip and Taken with Teal Classic pads; paper crimper; Creamy Caramel eyelets; Natural hemp; thread

17 C
Very Merry and Season's Greetings sets; Forest Foliage, Baroque Burgundy, Ultrasmooth Vanilla, Old Olive, and Radiant White vellum card stock; Basic Black, Forest Foliage, Close to Cocoa, Baroque Burgundy, More Mustard, and Old Olive Classic pads; watercolor brush; Burgundy wide organdy ribbon; Silver star eyelets; Stampin' Dimensionals; needle

17 D
Very Merry and Season's Greetings sets; Forest Foliage, Baroque Burgundy, Old Olive, Naturals Ivory, and Ultrasmooth Vanilla card stock; Basic Black, Old Olive, Forest Foliage, Baroque Burgundy, Creamy Caramel, and Really Rust Classic pads; watercolor brush; Old Olive and Baroque Burgundy eyelets; Stampin' Dimensionals; Burgundy wide organdy ribbon; string

18 A
Bold Shapes, Petite Patterns, and All-Year Cheer I sets; Ruby Red, Mellow Moss, and Ultrasmooth Vanilla card stock; Mellow Moss, Basic Black, and Really Rust Classic pads; watercolor brush; Stampin' Dimensionals; Mellow Moss and Really Rust eyelets; sewing machine with thread; jute

18 B
Bold Shapes and Fun Phrases sets; Basic Black, Bordering Blue, Ruby Red, and Ultrasmooth White card stock; Basic Black, Ruby Red, and Bordering Blue Classic pads; Basic Black marker; Stampin' Dimensionals; Silver Mini Deco Fasteners; button

18 C
Little Hellos and Bold Alphabet sets; Bordering Blue, Mellow Moss, Barely Banana, and Ultrasmooth Vanilla card stock; Basic Black, Mellow Moss, Barely Banana, and Bordering Blue Classic pads; watercolor brush; Scallop scissors; Stampin' Dimensionals; Mellow Moss, Barely Banana, and Bordering Blue eyelets; buttons; string

18 D
Little Hellos set; Mellow Moss, Ruby Red, and Confetti White card stock; Basic Black, Really Rust, Mellow Moss, Blush Blossom, Mauve Mist, and Bordering Blue Classic pads; watercolor brush; Stampin' Dimensionals; 1/8" Circle punch; Gold metallic cord; Mellow Moss eyelets

19 A
All Natural set; Mellow Moss, Ruby Red, Bordering Blue, and Confetti White card stock; Bordering Blue and Basic Black Classic pads; watercolor brush; Stampin' Dimensionals; Natural hemp; needle

19 B
Memory of the Heart set; Bordering Blue and Confetti White card stock; Bordering Blue and Really Rust Classic pads; Rectangle punch; Bluebird grosgrain ribbon; Silver metallic cord

19 C
Memory of the Heart and Birthday Greetings sets; Bordering Blue, Ruby Red, and Confetti White card stock; White mulberry paper (dyed with Bordering Blue Classic ink); Bordering Blue and Really Rust Classic pads; Lace Corner punch; Rectangle punch; French Blue grosgrain ribbon; Bordering Blue eyelet; Silver metallic cord; Stampin' Dimensionals

19 D
Memory of the Heart set; Hand-Stitched background stamp; Barely Banana, Bordering Blue, Night of Navy, and Confetti White card stock; Confetti White tag sheet; Basic Black, Barely Banana, Bordering Blue, Old Olive, Really Rust, Going Gray, and Not Quite Navy Classic pads; watercolor brush; Southwest Corner punch; Stampin' Dimensionals; French Blue grosgrain ribbon; string

20 A
Nature Sketchbook and All-Year Cheer I sets; Lovely Lilac card stock; Old Olive tag sheet; Confetti White pouch box; Basic Black, Lovely Lilac, More Mustard, Only Orange, and Old Olive Classic pads; watercolor brush; More Mustard eyelet; Stampin' Dimensionals; string

20 B
Nature Sketchbook set; More Mustard, Old Olive, Confetti White, and Kraft card stock; Basic Black, Old Olive, More Mustard, and Creamy Caramel Classic pads; watercolor brush; Stampin' Dimensionals; stamping sponge; Spring Moss grosgrain ribbon; sewing machine and thread

20 C
Nature Sketchbook set; Old Olive, Radiant White vellum, Confetti White, Confetti Tan, and Basic Black card stock; Confetti White tag sheet; Red mulberry paper; Basic Black Classic ink; watercolor brushes; raffia; Stampin' Dimensionals

21 A
Greetings Galore set; Real Red, Kraft, Lovely Lilac, and Confetti White card stock; Basic Black, Real Red, Only Orange, Lovely Lilac, and Old Olive Classic pads; watercolor brush; 1/2" and 1/16" Circle punches; Silver Mini Deco Fastener; Scallop scissors; Stampin' Dimensionals; Delphinium grosgrain ribbon; string

21 B
Greetings Galore set; Old Olive, Ultrasmooth Vanilla, and Kraft card stock; More Mustard tag sheet; Old Olive and More Mustard Classic pads; watercolor brush; More Mustard and Old Olive eyelets; Stampin' Dimensionals; jute; sewing machine and thread

21 C
Greetings Galore and Fresh Fillers sets; Kraft, Old Olive, Confetti White, and Real Red card stock; Basic Black, More Mustard, Old Olive, and Real Red Classic pads; watercolor brush; Stampin' Dimensionals; Real Red eyelets; Natural hemp

22 A
Hearts & Posies and Classic Alphabet sets; Rose Romance, Real Red, and Ultrasmooth White card stock; Rose Romance and Real Red Craft pads; Stampin' Dimensionals; crochet thread; needle

22 B
Love Ya! set; Real Red, Eggplant Envy, and Ultrasmooth White card stock; Real Red and Eggplant Envy Classic pads; Stampin' Dimensionals; Real Red heart eyelet; Purple hemp

23 A
Happy Hearts and All-Year Cheer I sets; Groovy Lines background stamp; Rose Romance, Real Red, and Ultrasmooth White card stock; Rose Romance and Real Red Classic pads; Stampin' Dimensionals; 26-gauge Wire Works; Silver eyelets; 1/16" Circle punch

23 B
Happy Hearts and Quirky Alphabet Upper sets; Groovy Lines background stamp; Rose Romance, Ultrasmooth White, and Pretty in Pink card stock; Rose Romance Craft pad; VersaMark pad; Stampin' Dimensionals; font CD; Pretty in Pink eyelets; beads

23 C
Sweetheart Candy II set; By Definition background stamp; Rose Romance, Real Red, and Ultrasmooth White card stock; Eggplant Envy, Rose Romance, and Real Red Classic pads; 22-gauge Wire Works; Real Red large circle eyelet; crochet thread; needle

24 A
Bear Hugs set; Rose Romance and Confetti White card stock; Basic Black and Baroque Burgundy Classic pads; watercolor brush; 1/16" and 1/4" Circle punches; Natural hemp

24 B
Be Mine set; Soft Swirls background stamp; Rose Romance, Barely Banana, and Confetti White card stock; Basic Black, Barely Banana, Old Olive, Creamy Caramel, Going Gray, Rose Romance, and Pretty in Pink Classic pads; watercolor brush; Stampin' Dimensionals; Rectangle punch; Rose grosgrain ribbon; Positively Pink eyelets; string

24 C
Be Mine set; Rose Romance, Confetti White, and Mellow Moss card stock; Basic Black, Real Red, Barely Banana, Blush Blossom, Positively Pink, Going Gray, Creamy Caramel, Close to Cocoa, Mellow Moss, and Bordering Blue Classic pads; watercolor brush; 1/8" Circle punch; Real Red heart eyelets; Natural hemp; Stampin' Dimensionals

25 A
Vintage Postcard, Little Shapes, and The Shape of Things sets; Confetti Cream card stock; Basic Black, Mellow Moss, Baroque Burgundy, and Bordering Blue Classic pads; journaling marker; stipple brush

25 B
True Love set; French Script background stamp; Bordering Blue, Confetti Cream, and Baroque Burgundy card stock; Burgundy mulberry paper; Basic Black, Bordering Blue, Baroque Burgundy, and Old Olive Classic pads; watercolor brush; Stampin' Dimensionals; Ivory narrow organdy ribbon

25 C
True Love set; French Script background stamp; Baroque Burgundy, Bordering Blue, Radiant White vellum, and Confetti Cream card stock; Burgundy and Mauve mulberry paper; Basic Black, Baroque Burgundy, and Bordering Blue Classic pads; Gold Encore! pad; watercolor brush; stipple brush; stamping sponge; 1/16" Circle punch; Stampin' Dimensionals; Gold metallic cord

26 A
Animal Valentines and Little Shapes sets; Ultrasmooth White, Green Galore, and Real Red card stock; Basic Black, Gable Green, Green Galore, and Real Red Classic pads; VersaMark pad; watercolor brush; Stampin' Dimensionals; 22-gauge Wire Works; Real Red eyelets; Apple Green grosgrain ribbon; Crystal Clear embossing powder

26 B
Be Mine and All-Year Cheer I sets; Green Galore, Ultrasmooth White, and Real Red card stock; Real Red tag sheet; Basic Black, Green Galore, Real Red, and Going Gray Classic pads; watercolor brush; Real Red eyelets; 22-gauge Wire Works; Crystal Effects

26 C
Have A Heart and All-Year Cheer I sets; Positively Pink, Green Galore, Ultrasmooth White, and Lovely Lilac card stock; Ultrasmooth White tag sheet; Basic Black, Lovely Lilac, Green Galore, Only Orange, and Positively Pink Classic pads; watercolor brush; Stampin' Dimensionals; 1/16" Circle punch; 22-gauge Wire Works

27 A
Hearts & Clovers and Good Times sets; Lovely Lilac, Gable Green, Positively Pink, and Confetti White card stock; Basic Black, Gable Green, Green Galore, Lovely Lilac, Positively Pink, and Summer Sun Classic pads; watercolor brush; paper crimper; Silver Mini Deco Fasteners

27 B
Hearts & Clovers set; Gable Green, Green Galore, and Confetti White card stock; Glorious Green Square AlphaAccents; Gable Green and Green Galore Classic pads; Glorious Green marker; watercolor brush; Green Galore eyelets; crochet thread

27 C
Spring Gifts and All-Year Cheer I sets; Ultrasmooth White and Lovely Lilac card stock; Basic Black, Rose Romance, Green Galore, Lovely Lilac, and Summer Sun Classic pads; Stampin' Dimensionals; Purple wide organdy ribbon

27 D
Spring Gifts set; Spring Things wheel; Green Galore, Lovely Lilac, Real Red, and Ultrasmooth White card stock; Basic Black, Real Red, Only Orange, Lovely Lilac, Green Galore, and Positively Pink Classic pads; Coal Black cartridge; Positively Pink marker; air art tool; paper crimper; Real Red, Lovely Lilac, and Positively Pink large flower eyelets; Only Orange eyelets; watercolor brush

28 A
Miracle of Spring set; Checkerboard background stamp; Mellow Moss and Ultrasmooth White card stock; Candy Designer Series vellum; Basic Black and Mellow Moss Classic pads; watercolor brush; Mellow Moss eyelet; White narrow organdy ribbon

28 B
Eggcitement and Quirky Alphabet Upper sets; Pretty in Pink, Radiant White vellum, and Ultrasmooth White card stock; Candy Designer Series paper; White Craft pad; journaling marker; Winter White embossing powder; Pretty in Pink eyelets; Positively Pink large flower eyelet; vellum circle metal edge tag; White narrow organdy ribbon

29 A
Spring Party set; Joy of Spring wheel; Ultrasmooth White, Blush Blossom, and Mellow Moss card stock; Mellow Moss and Blush Blossom Classic pads; Mellow Moss cartridge; watercolor brush; Mellow Moss eyelets; Olive Green wide organdy ribbon

29 B
Loving Memories set; Lavender Lace, Blush Blossom, and Ultrasmooth White card stock; Lavender mulberry paper; Lavender Lace, Blush Blossom, Old Olive, and Pretty in Pink Classic pads; VersaMark pad; watercolor brush; Winter White embossing powder

29 C
Spring Party set; Lavender Lace, Mellow Moss, and Ultrasmooth White card stock; VersaMark pad; Stampin' Pastels; Lavender Lace eyelets

30 A
Renewed Faith set; Brocade Blue, Barely Banana, and Ultrasmooth White card stock; Splash Designer Series vellum; Brocade Blue and Barely Banana Classic pads; Blue narrow organdy ribbon

30 B
Renewed Faith set; Brocade Blue, Barely Banana, and Ultrasmooth White card stock; Brocade Blue Classic pad; Brocade Blue, Barely Banana, and Mellow Moss Classic ink refills; empty Spectrum pad; Barely Banana eyelet

30 C
The Gifts of Spring set; Mellow Moss, Barely Banana, and Ultrasmooth White card stock; Splash Designer Series paper; Mellow Moss, Basic Black, Barely Banana, Almost Amethyst, Lavender Lace, Orchid Opulence, and Gable Green Classic pads; watercolor brush; Stampin' Dimensionals; Cream grosgrain ribbon

31 A
Tropical Fish and Classic Alphabet sets; Green Galore, Ultrasmooth White, and Ballet Blue card stock; Ultrasmooth White tag sheets; Ballet Blue and Green Galore Craft pads; Green Galore eyelets; Stampin' Dimensionals; font CD; crochet thread

31 B
Tropical Fish set; Ballet Blue, Barely Banana, and Green Galore card stock; Splash Designer Series vellum; Green Galore and Ballet Blue Classic pads; font CD; Barely Banana eyelet; 26-gauge Wire Works; Stampin' Dimensionals; string

32 A
Leapfrogs, Brushstroke Alphabet, and Alphabet Fun Uppers sets; Not Quite Navy, Barely Banana, Garden Green, and More Mustard card stock; Splash Designer Series vellum and paper; Not Quite Navy and Garden Green Craft pads; Crystal Clear embossing powder; 1/8" Circle punch; Green hemp; font CD

32 B
Leapfrogs and Little Letters sets; Garden Green, Barely Banana, Not Quite Navy, and More Mustard card stock; Garden Green Classic pad; Stampin' Pastels; More Mustard and Night of Navy eyelets; Gold hemp; Stampin' Dimensionals

33 A
Fly Fishing and Perfect Plaids sets; Not Quite Navy and Barely Banana card stock; medium kraft gable box; Chocolate Chip, Not Quite Navy, and More Mustard Craft pads; watercolor brush; stamping sponge; 1/8" Circle punch; More Mustard eyelets; Gold hemp

33 B
Stipple Shells, The Shape of Things, and All-Around Alphabet sets; Not Quite Navy, More Mustard, and Barely Banana card stock; Not Quite Navy, More Mustard, and Chocolate Chip Classic pads; Barely Banana Craft pad; Gold Encore! pad; VersaMark pad; journaling marker; Crystal Clear embossing powder; Gold Mini Deco Fasteners; 26-gauge Wire Works; bleach; beads

33 C
All-Year Cheer I set; By the Sea wheel; More Mustard and Chocolate Chip card stock; Chocolate Chip cartridge; Barely Banana Craft pad; Gold wide organdy ribbon; 26-gauge Wire Works; shells; beads

34 A
Roughing It and Classic Alphabet sets; Confetti Tan, Old Olive, Real Red, Night of Navy, and Ultrasmooth Vanilla card stock; Real Red, Close to Cocoa, Old Olive, and Night of Navy Craft pads; journaling marker; 1/16" Circle punch; Natural hemp; buttons

34 B
Roughing It and Classic Alphabet sets; Night of Navy, Old Olive, and Ultrasmooth Vanilla card stock; Real Red, Night of Navy, Close to Cocoa, and Old Olive Classic pads; Basic Black marker; Natural hemp; button

35 A
Stars & Swirls and Classic Alphabet sets; Confetti Tan, Ultrasmooth Vanilla, Old Olive, and Night of Navy card stock; Night of Navy Classic pad; 1/16" Circle punch; Natural hemp

35 B
Stars & Swirls set; Real Red, Night of Navy, Confetti Tan, and Ultrasmooth Vanilla card stock; Night of Navy, Real Red, and Creamy Caramel Classic pads; Real Red star eyelet; Stampin' Dimensionals; Natural hemp

35 C
I Love Canada set; Confetti Tan, Ultrasmooth Vanilla, and Real Red card stock; Real Red Classic pad; Natural hemp; 1/16" Circle punch

36 A
Star-Spangled Day set; Confetti White, Brilliant Blue, Real Red, and Summer Sun card stock; Basic Black, Blush Blossom, Brilliant Blue, Real Red, Creamy Caramel, Going Gray, and Summer Sun Classic pads; watercolor brush; Stampin' Dimensionals; 1/16" Circle punch; crochet string; button

36 B
Country Fresh and All-Year Cheer I sets; Checkerboard background stamp; Confetti White, Real Red, Basic Black, and Brilliant Blue card stock; Confetti White and Real Red tag sheets; Basic Black, Real Red, and Brilliant Blue Classic pads; Stampin' Dimensionals; crochet thread; needle

36 C
Country Fresh and Simple Sayings II sets; Chicken Wire background stamp; Confetti White, Summer Sun, Brilliant Blue, and Real Red card stock; Basic Black, Summer Sun, Brilliant Blue, Bliss Blue, Real Red, Gable Green, and Creamy Caramel Classic pads; 1/16" Circle punch; watercolor brush; Black hemp

37 A
Summer Fun and Bold Alphabet sets; Only Orange, Summer Sun, Basic Black, and Ultrasmooth Vanilla card stock; Only Orange and Summer Sun Craft pads; font CD; Black and Only Orange eyelets; Gold hemp; sewing machine and thread

37 B
Tickled Pink set; Ultrasmooth Vanilla, Green Galore, Lovely Lilac, and Cameo Coral card stock; Cameo Coral, Basic Black, Lovely Lilac, and Glorious Green Classic pads; VersaMark pad; Black detail embossing powder; watercolor brush; Stampin' Dimensionals; 26-gauge Wire Works; Green Galore and Lovely Lilac eyelets; 1/8" Circle punch; Natural hemp

38 A
Just Flying By and All-Year Cheer III sets; Only Orange, Summer Sun, and Ultrasmooth Vanilla card stock; Basic Black, Summer Sun, and Only Orange Classic pads; watercolor brush; Southwest Corner punch; Crystal Effects; Stampin' Dimensionals; 22-gauge Wire Works

38 B
Just Flying By set; Basic Black, Only Orange, Confetti Cream, Summer Sun, Green Galore, and Lovely Lilac card stock; Basic Black, Lovely Lilac, Green Galore, Only Orange, Blush Blossom, Summer Sun, and Creamy Caramel Classic pads; watercolor brush

38 C
Tricky Treats set; Basic Black, Confetti Cream, and Green Galore card stock; Confetti Cream tag sheet; Basic Black and Green Galore Classic pads; Stampin' Pastels; 1/16" and 1/4" Circle punches; Stampin' Dimensionals; Black hemp; wiggle eyes

39 A
Bitty Boos set; Basic Black, Green Galore, Pink Passion, and Ultrasmooth White card stock; Lovely Lilac, Pink Passion, and Green Galore Square AlphaAccents; Ultrasmooth White Circle AlphaAccents Jrs.; Stampin' Dimensionals; watercolor brush; 1/8" Circle punch; Delphinium, Rose, and Apple Green grosgrain ribbon; button; thread; needle

39 B
Trick or Treat and Itty Bitty Backgrounds sets; Groovy Lines background stamp; Lovely Lilac, Basic Black, Green Galore, Ultrasmooth White, and Only Orange card stock; Basic Black, Only Orange, and Lovely Lilac classic pads; Green Galore and Only Orange triangle eyelets; 22-gauge Wire Works; 1/8" Circle punch; Stampin' Dimensionals; Black hemp; Black embroidery floss; needle

39 C
Trick or Treat, Alphabet Fun Upper, and Alphabet Fun Lower sets; Only Orange, Basic Black, Green Galore, and Summer Sun card stock; White and Basic Black Craft pads; VersaMark pad; journaling marker; Black and Lovely Lilac eyelets

40 A
Costume Bears and All-Year Cheer I sets; Swirls background stamp; Lovely Lilac, Basic Black, Confetti White, and Eggplant Envy card stock; Basic Black, Only Orange, Lovely Lilac, Eggplant Envy, Garden Green, and Close to Cocoa Classic pads; watercolor brush; Confetti White tag sheet; Black grosgrain ribbon; Silver Mini Deco Fasteners

40 B
Halloween Hedgehogs set; Basic Black, Only Orange, and Lovely Lilac card stock; VersaMark pad; Basic Black, Only Orange, Lovely Lilac, Summer Sun, Positively Pink, and Close to Cocoa Classic pads; watercolor brush; Black detail embossing powder; Stampin' Dimensionals; Black grosgrain ribbon; bleach

41 A
Halloween Smiles set; Kraft, Basic Black, Eggplant Envy, and Only Orange card stock; VersaMark pad; Basic Black Classic pad; Summer Sun, Only Orange, Garden Green, Eggplant Envy, and Basic Black Craft pads; watercolor brush; Black eyelets; Natural hemp; Stampin' Dimensionals; bleach

41 B
Grinning Ghouls and Classic Alphabet sets; Basic Black, Eggplant Envy, and Lovely Lilac card stock; VersaMark pad; Basic Black Craft pad; journaling marker; Stampin' Pastels; Black embossing powder; blender pens; Stampin' Dimensionals; Black hemp; bleach

42 A
Spooktacular Greetings set; Eggplant Envy, Basic Black, Confetti White, and Old Olive card stock; Basic Black, Going Gray, More Mustard, and Old Olive Classic pads; watercolor brush

42 B
Fall Fun set; Old Olive, Eggplant Envy, Really Rust, More Mustard, Mellow Moss, and Confetti Cream card stock; Eggplant Envy Classic pad; Late November Spectrum pad; Perfect Plum eyelet; Natural hemp; 1/16" Circle punch; Stampin' Dimensionals

42 C
All-Year Cheer I set; Harvest wheel; Really Rust, Chocolate Chip, More Mustard, and Naturals Ivory card stock; Really Rust Classic pad; VersaMark pad; Stampin' Pastels; Really Rust eyelets

43 A
Happy Fall, Y'all set; Perfect Plum, More Mustard, and Ultrasmooth Vanilla card stock; Creamy Caramel, More Mustard, Perfect Plum, Chocolate Chip, Blush Blossom, Going Gray, Old Olive, Summer Sun, and Close to Cocoa Classic pads; VersaMark pad; watercolor brush; Black detail embossing powder; More Mustard eyelets; raffia

43 B
Fall Whimsy and Simple Sayings II sets; Old Olive, More Mustard, Naturals White, and Perfect Plum card stock; Basic Black, Only Orange, Barely Banana, More Mustard, Ruby Red, Perfect Plum, and Old Olive Classic pads; watercolor brush

43 C
Fall Whimsy and Brushstroke Alphabet set; Acorn wheel; Mellow Moss, Eggplant Envy, More Mustard, and Ruby Red card stock; Basic Black Craft pad; Mellow Moss cartridge; font CD

44 A
Turkey Talk and All-Year Cheer I sets; More Mustard, Old Olive, and Naturals Ivory card stock; Olive Green mulberry paper; Basic Black, More Mustard, Only Orange, Creamy Caramel, Eggplant Envy, Really Rust, More Mustard, and Mellow Moss Classic pads; Stampin' Dimensionals; 1/16" Circle punch; Natural hemp; buttons; twig; crochet thread

44 B
Fantastic Foliage and Fun Phrases sets; Ultrasmooth Vanilla, More Mustard, and Old Olive card stock; VersaMark pad; More Mustard, Really Rust, Old Olive, and Basic Black Classic pads; watercolor brush; Crystal Clear embossing powder; stamping sponge; More Mustard square eyelets; crochet thread; needle

44 C
Fantastic Foliage and Simple Sayings II sets; Old Olive, Garden Green, Confetti Cream, Radiant White vellum, and Ultrasmooth Vanilla card stock; Basic Black, Old Olive, Garden Green, Mellow Moss, Sage Shadow, and Forest Foliage Classic pads; watercolor brush; Natural hemp; Cream grosgrain ribbon

45 A
Season of Thanks set; Perfect Plum, More Mustard, and Confetti Cream card stock; Perfect Plum, Basic Black, More Mustard, Old Olive, and Creamy Caramel Classic pads; watercolor brush; paper crimper; Perfect Plum eyelets; Natural hemp

45 B
Festive Fall, The Shape of Things, Little Shapes, and Simple Sayings sets; More Mustard, Confetti Cream, Ruby Red, and Old Olive card stock; Old Olive and More Mustard Classic pads; Festive Fall brass template; Stampin' Dimensionals; 1/16" Circle punch; Natural hemp; bleach

45 C
Festive Fall set; Confetti Cream, Mellow Moss, Radiant White vellum, Ruby Red, and Old Olive card stock; Basic Black, Old Olive, Mellow Moss, Really Rust, and More Mustard Classic pads; watercolor brush; Ivory narrow organdy ribbon; Gold Mini Deco Fasteners

46 A
Festive Hanukkah set; Night of Navy and Brushed Silver card stock; Silver Encore! pad; VersaMarker; Sterling Silver embossing powder; 26-gauge Wire Works; paper crimper

46 B
Mazel Tov set; Night of Navy, Almost Amethyst, and Radiant White vellum card stock; VersaMark pad; Sterling Silver embossing powder

46 C
Mazel Tov set; Night of Navy and Almost Amethyst card stock; VersaMark pad; Sterling Silver embossing powder; Silver metallic cord; beads

47 A
Winter Wonderland set; Almost Amethyst, Night of Navy, and Brushed Silver card stock; White mulberry paper; Victorian Designer Series vellum; Night of Navy Classic pad; Stampin' Dimensionals; Dazzling Diamonds glitter; 1/16" Circle punch; Silver metallic cord

47 B
Sleigh Ride set; Garden Green, Real Red, Almost Amethyst, and Naturals White card stock; Basic Black, Almost Amethyst, Garden Green, Chocolate Chip, Going Gray, Real Red, Forest Foliage, Yoyo Yellow, Night of Navy, and Creamy Caramel Classic pads; watercolor brush; Stampin' Dimensionals; Red grosgrain ribbon; Dazzling Diamonds glitter

48 A
Christmas Gift Tags set; Forest Foliage, Ultrasmooth White, Baroque Burgundy, and More Mustard card stock; Forest Foliage, Baroque Burgundy, and More Mustard markers; Baroque Burgundy eyelet; Red hemp

48 B
Christmas Gift Tags set; Baroque Burgundy, Night of Navy, and Ultrasmooth White card stock; Baroque Burgundy, Forest Foliage, and Night of Navy markers; Forest Foliage eyelets; Natural hemp

48 C
Happy Winter set; Night of Navy, Baroque Burgundy, Creamy Caramel, and Ultrasmooth White card stock; Baroque Burgundy, Creamy Caramel, and Basic Black Classic pads; watercolor brush; 22-gauge Wire Works

49 A
Old-Fashioned Christmas set; Night of Navy, Creamy Caramel, Baroque Burgundy, Confetti White, and Forest Foliage card stock; VersaMark pad; Forest Foliage, More Mustard, Baroque Burgundy, Night of Navy, Close to Cocoa, Bordering Blue, Creamy Caramel, and Summer Sun Classic pads; watercolor brush; Black detail embossing powder

49 B
Snow Globe set; Baroque Burgundy, Forest Foliage, Night of Navy, Creamy Caramel, and Ultrasmooth White card stock; Basic Black, Bordering Blue, Baroque Burgundy, Creamy Caramel, and Forest Foliage Classic pads; White Craft pad; Taupe grosgrain ribbon; watercolor brush

50 A
Festive Friends and All-Year Cheer I sets; Real Red, Garden Green, Ultrasmooth White, and Night of Navy card stock; More Mustard, Positively Pink, Basic Black, Real Red, Night of Navy, and Garden Green Classic pads; watercolor brush; Natural hemp; buttons

50 B

Holiday Sampler set; Garden Green, Ultrasmooth White, Night of Navy, and Real Red card stock; Real Red and Garden Green Classic pads; Stampin' Dimensionals; Night of Navy eyelets; Red grosgrain ribbon

50 C

Holiday Sampler set; Real Red, Ultrasmooth White, Night of Navy, and Garden Green card stock; Real Red and Night of Navy tag sheets; Garden Green and Real Red Classic pads; 1/4" and 1/2" Circle punches; Real Red eyelet; Natural hemp

51 A

Crayon Christmas and Crayon Fun Alphabet sets; Real Red, More Mustard, Night of Navy, Ultrasmooth White, and Garden Green card stock; Ultrasmooth White tag sheets; Real Red and Garden Green Craft pads; Real Red marker; Natural hemp; 1/8" Circle punch; buttons

51 B

Season's Sketches and Classic Alphabet sets; More Mustard, Garden Green, Night of Navy, Real Red, and Ultrasmooth White card stock; Garden Green and More Mustard Classic pads

52 A

A Merry Season set; Hand-Stitched background stamp; Real Red, Brilliant Blue, Confetti Cream, and Old Olive card stock; Basic Black and Real Red Classic pads; Stampin' Pastels; Old Olive oval eyelets; Red grosgrain ribbon; 1/8" Circle punch; Stampin' Dimensionals; button

52 B

Flaky Friends set; Brilliant Blue, Real Red, Old Olive, and Confetti Cream card stock; Brilliant Blue, Basic Black, Going Gray, Real Red, More Mustard, and Bordering Blue Classic pads; watercolor brush; Old Olive eyelets; Stampin' Dimensionals; crochet thread

52 C

Flaky Friends and All-Year Cheer I sets; Old Olive, More Mustard, Real Red, and Confetti Cream card stock; Basic Black, More Mustard, Old Olive, and Creamy Caramel Classic pads; watercolor brush; Stampin' Dimensionals; Old Olive eyelets; Natural hemp

53 A

Ho-Ho-Holidays set; Real Red, Brilliant Blue, Old Olive, and Confetti Cream card stock; Basic Black, Real Red, Brilliant Blue, More Mustard, Old Olive, and Blush Blossom Classic pads; watercolor brush; Old Olive eyelet; Natural hemp; Stampin' Dimensionals; crochet thread; button

53 B

Ho-Ho-Holidays set; Real Red, Brilliant Blue, Confetti Cream, and Old Olive card stock; Basic Black, More Mustard, Real Red, Old Olive, and Creamy Caramel Classic pads; watercolor brush; Brilliant Blue star eyelets; Real Red eyelet; Red grosgrain ribbon

53 C

Merry Elves set; Old Olive, Brilliant Blue, Real Red, and Confetti White card sock; Basic Black, Creamy Caramel, More Mustard, Blush Blossom, Rose Romance, Brilliant Blue, Old Olive, and Real Red Classic pads; watercolor brush; Old Olive eyelets

53 D

Merry Elves set; Confetti White, Brilliant Blue, Real Red, and Old Olive card stock; Basic Black, Old Olive, More Mustard, Creamy Caramel, Blush Blossom, Rose Romance, Brilliant Blue, and Real Red Classic pads; watercolor brush; Gold eyelet; Gold Mini Deco Fasteners; Red grosgrain ribbon

54 A

Holiday Hedgehogs and Little Shapes sets; Baroque Burgundy and Confetti White card stock; Baroque Burgundy, Forest Foliage, and Basic Black Classic pads; Burgundy wide organdy ribbon; Red hemp; watercolor brush; Baroque Burgundy eyelet; white wrapping paper

54 B

Holiday Wishes set; Brushed Gold and Forest Foliage card stock; VersaMark pad; Gold detail embossing powder; Southwest Corner punch; Gold eyelets; Gold metallic cord; Stampin' Dimensionals

54 C

Holiday Wishes set; Gifts Galore wheel; Brushed Gold, Forest Foliage, and Confetti White card stock; Confetti White party favor box; Forest Foliage Classic pad; Forest Foliage cartridge; Gold eyelet; Gold metallic cord; 1/16" Circle punch

55 A

Frosty set; Snowman Fun wheel; Brocade Blue, Ballet Blue, and Confetti Cream card stock; Basic Black, Bliss Blue, Baroque Burgundy, Going Gray, Only Orange, Forest Foliage, and Close to Cocoa Classic pads; Brocade Blue cartridge; watercolor brush; French Blue grosgrain ribbon

55 B

Holiday Woodcuts set; Stipple Plaid background stamp; Baroque Burgundy, More Mustard, Forest Foliage, and Confetti White card stock; Confetti White and Forest Foliage tag sheets; Baroque Burgundy Classic pad; Stampin' Dimensionals; Forest Foliage eyelets; crochet thread; needle

55 C

Holiday Woodcuts set; Confetti White card stock; Baroque Burgundy and Forest Foliage tag sheets; Forest Foliage and Baroque Burgundy Classic pads; Basic Black marker; Stampin' Dimensionals; 26-gauge Wire Works; Silver metallic cord; Silver eyelet

56 A

Miracle of Christmas set; Filigree background stamp; Brocade Blue, Bordering Blue, Ultrasmooth Vanilla, and Barely Banana card stock; Basic Black and Bordering Blue Classic pads; Stampin' Pastels; Southwest Corner punch; Stampin' Dimensionals; 1/8" Circle punch; Ivory narrow organdy ribbon

56 B

Season of Peace set; Brocade Blue, Ruby Red, Ballet Blue, and Mellow Moss card stock; Brocade Blue, Ballet Blue, and Mellow Moss Classic pads; Stampin' Dimensionals; 1/16" Circle punch; Natural hemp

56 C

Season of Peace set; Brocade Blue, Ballet Blue, Bordering Blue, and Confetti White card stock; Basic Black, Bordering Blue, Ballet Blue, and Brocade Blue Classic pads; watercolor brush; Stampin' Dimensionals; Bordering Blue eyelets; Silver metallic cord

57 A

Christmas Foliage set; Mellow Moss, Ruby Red, Ultrasmooth Vanilla, and Radiant White vellum card stock; VersaMark pad; Ruby Red and Mellow Moss Classic pads; watercolor brush; Gold Glory embossing powder; Gold Mini Deco Fasteners; Gold metallic ribbon; Stampin' Dimensionals; bleach

57 B

Jolly Old Elf and All-Year Cheer I sets; Ruby Red, Old Olive, Creamy Caramel, and Confetti Cream card stock; Basic Black, Bordering Blue, Ruby Red, Old Olive, Really Rust, Creamy Caramel, and Blush Blossom Classic pads; watercolor brush; Stampin' Dimensionals; Southwest Corner punch; sewing machine and thread; crochet thread; needle

57 C

Jolly Old Elf set; Confetti Cream, Brocade Blue, Ruby Red, Ultrasmooth Vanilla, and Mellow Moss card stock; Ruby Red, Basic Black, Brocade Blue, Blush Blossom, Summer Sun, and Mellow Moss Classic pads; White Craft pad; Basic Black marker; watercolor brush; vellum circle metal edge tag; 1/8" Circle punch; Stampin' Dimensionals; Bordering Blue eyelet; Folk Star punch; 26-gauge Wire Works

58 A

Enchanted Snowflakes set; Confetti White, Radiant White vellum, Baroque Burgundy, and Mellow Moss card stock; White Craft pad; Basic Black and Baroque Burgundy Classic pads; More Mustard, Baroque Burgundy, Bordering Blue, and Mellow Moss markers; Gold Mini Deco Fasteners; 1/16" Circle punch; Regal Tones fiber

58 B

Enchanted Snowflakes set; Bordering Blue, Confetti White, and Mellow Moss card stock; Confetti White tag sheet; White and Celery mulberry paper; Basic Black, Night of Navy, Mellow Moss, More Mustard, and Baroque Burgundy Classic pads; watercolor brush; Stampin' Dimensionals; White large circle eyelet; Bordering Blue eyelet; Silver metallic cord; Silver Mini Deco Fasteners; Neutrals fiber

58 C

The Spirit of Love set; Ultrasmooth Vanilla, Baroque Burgundy, and Mellow Moss card stock; Baroque Burgundy Classic pad; Burgundy and Celery mulberry paper; watercolor brush; Moss grosgrain ribbon

58 D

Snowy Trees wheel; Bordering Blue, Confetti White, and Mellow Moss card stock; Bordering Blue cartridge; Stampin' Pastels; White large circle eyelet; Bordering Blue and Mellow Moss eyelets; Silver wide organdy ribbon; Silver metallic cord

59 A

Angelic and God Bless sets; Naturals Ivory, Baroque Burgundy, Mellow Moss, and Ultrasmooth Vanilla card stock; Burgundy mulberry paper; Baroque Burgundy and Mellow Moss Classic pads; watercolor brush; Burgundy wide organdy ribbon; Gold metallic cord; Gold eyelet; 1/8" Circle punch

59 B

Angelic set; Victorian Lace background stamp; Ultrasmooth Vanilla, Mellow Moss, and Baroque Burgundy card stock; Baroque Burgundy and Mellow Moss Classic pads; Baroque Burgundy marker; air art tool; 1/8" Circle punch; Gold metallic cord; Olive Green wide organdy ribbon; Stampin' Dimensionals

59 C

All-Year Cheer I set; Heart Angels wheel; Bordering Blue, Perfect Plum, Mellow Moss, and Confetti White card stock; Basic Black, Perfect Plum, Barely Banana, and Bordering Blue Classic pads; Bordering Blue cartridge; watercolor brush; 1/16" and 1/8" Circle punches; Southwest Corner punch; Stampin' Dimensionals; crochet thread

60 A

Star of Wonder set; Musical Score background stamp; More Mustard, Not Quite Navy, and Ultrasmooth Vanilla card stock; Not Quite Navy Classic pad; Gold metallic cord; Stampin' Dimensionals; beads

60 B

Peace on Earth set; Real Red, Ultrasmooth Vanilla, and Not Quite Navy card stock; Gold Encore! pad; Not Quite Navy and Creamy Caramel Classic pads; watercolor brush; Gold Glory embossing powder; Gold metallic ribbon; Gold eyelet

60 C

Peace on Earth set; Brushed Gold card stock; Ultrasmooth Vanilla and Forest Foliage tag sheets; Forest Foliage Classic pads; Gold eyelet; Ivory narrow organdy ribbon

61 A

A Beautiful Season set; Not Quite Navy, Real Red, Ultrasmooth Vanilla, and Brushed Gold card stock; Red mulberry paper; VersaMark pad; Stampin' Pastels; 1/16" Circle punch; Natural hemp; twig

61 B

A Beautiful Season set; Ultrasmooth Vanilla and Real Red card stock; Not Quite Navy Craft pad; Gold eyelets; Gold metallic cord; Crystal Clear embossing powder

61 C

A Beautiful Season set; Not Quite Navy, Confetti White, and Chocolate Chip card stock; Chocolate Chip Classic pad; VersaMark pad; Stampin' Pastels; Stampin' Dimensionals; White wide organdy ribbon; White eyelets; Taupe grosgrain ribbon

62 A

Polar Bears and Itty Bitty Backgrounds sets; More Mustard, Ballet Blue, Confetti White, Glorious Green, and Real Red card stock; Basic Black, Real Red, More Mustard, and Ballet Blue Classic pads; Stampin' Dimensionals; watercolor brush

62 B

Polar Bears and Good Times sets; Soft Swirls background stamp; Ballet Blue, Real Red, and Confetti White card stock; Basic Black, Real Red, More Mustard, Ballet Blue, and Going Gray Classic pads; White Craft pad; watercolor brush; 1/2" and 1/16" Circle punches; Silver eyelet; Red grosgrain ribbon; 22-gauge Wire Works; Stampin' Dimensionals

62 C

Lace Snowflakes and All-Year Cheer I sets; Ballet Blue and Ultrasmooth White card stock; Ballet Blue Classic pad; Stampin' Dimensionals; Silver Mini Deco Fasteners; needle

63 A

Kris Kringle set; Real Red, Ballet Blue, Ultrasmooth White, and More Mustard card stock; Basic Black, Ballet Blue, More Mustard, Blush Blossom, Real Red, Baroque Burgundy, Close to Cocoa, Rose Romance, Garden Green, and Creamy Caramel Classic pads; watercolor brush; Ruby Red square eyelets; Square Steps Slot punch; Stampin' Dimensionals; Natural hemp

63 B

Season's Greetings set; Star wheel; Real Red, Ballet Blue, Ultrasmooth White, Summer Sun, and More Mustard card stock; die-cut basket box; More Mustard Classic pad; More Mustard cartridge; More Mustard eyelets; Red grosgrain ribbon; 26-gauge Wire Works; Stampin' Dimensionals

64 A

Winter Patches and All-year Cheer I sets; Real Red, Garden Green, and Ultrasmooth White card stock; Basic Black Craft pad; Real Red Classic pad; watercolor pencils; White PolyShrink; 1/8" Circle punch; Green hemp; button; red yarn; needle

64 B

Snow Angels set; Night of Navy, Real Red, and Ultrasmooth White card stock; Swirls printed vellum; Basic Black, Real Red, Blush Blossom, Night of Navy, Garden Green, Bordering Blue, Going Gray, and Creamy Caramel Classic pads; watercolor brush; white circle metal edge tag; Red grosgrain ribbon; 1/16" and 1/8" Circle punches; string

64 C
Snow Angels set; Winter Kids wheel; Real Red, Garden Green, and Ultrasmooth White card stock; Basic Black, Real Red, Garden Green, More Mustard, Creamy Caramel, Bordering Blue, Going Gray, Only Orange, Blush Blossom, and Positively Pink Classic pads; Real Red cartridge; watercolor brush; 1/16" Circle punch; Real Red eyelets; Green hemp; crochet thread; needle

65 A
Handstitched Holiday set; Real Red, Garden Green, Confetti White, and Radiant White vellum card stock; Basic Black, Real Red, Close to Cocoa, More Mustard, Garden Green, Bordering Blue, Only Orange, and Blush Blossom Classic pads; watercolor brush; Stampin' Dimensionals; Natural hemp; Forest Foliage eyelet; buttons

65 B
Sparkling Season set; Confetti White and Garden Green card stock; Real Red, Night of Navy, and Garden Green Classic pads; 1/16" Circle punch; Green hemp

66 A
Holiday Basics, By Design, and All-Year Cheer I sets; Real Red, Night of Navy, Garden Green, and Confetti White card stock; Confetti White tag sheet; Real Red, Garden Green, and Basic Black Classic pads; Stampin' Dimensionals; 26-gauge Wire Works; paper crimper; needle; crochet thread

66 B
Thanks Snow Much and Good Times sets; Garden Green, Brilliant Blue, Real Red, and Ultrasmooth White card stock; Ultrasmooth White tag sheet; Basic Black, Going Gray, Real Red, Brilliant Blue, Only Orange, and Garden Green Classic pads; watercolor brush; 1/16" Circle punch; Stampin' Dimensionals; Brilliant Blue eyelet; Blue hemp; crochet thread; needle

66 C
Thanks Snow Much set; Garden Green, Real Red, and Confetti White card stock; Basic Black, Garden Green, Going Gray, Real Red, and Only Orange Classic pads; watercolor brush; 1/16" Circle punch; Real Red eyelets; crochet thread

67 A
Crazy for Christmas, Little Letters, and All-Year Cheer I sets; Brilliant Blue, Real Red, and Confetti White card stock; Confetti White tag sheet; Basic Black, More Mustard, Brilliant Blue, Garden Green, and Real Red Classic pads; watercolor brush; Brilliant Blue eyelets; Stampin' Dimensionals; White grosgrain ribbon; crochet thread; button

67 B
Little Holiday Wishes set; Brilliant Blue, Ultrasmooth White, and Basic Black card stock; Real Red party favor box; Basic Black, Brilliant Blue, and Real Red Classic pads; watercolor brush; 1/16" Circle punch; white crochet thread

67 C
Crazy for Christmas set; Real Red, Confetti White, and Garden Green card stock; Basic Black, Garden Green, Forest Foliage, Real Red, and More Mustard Classic pads; watercolor brush; Black eyelets; Black hemp; buttons; crochet thread

67 D
Little Holiday Wishes set; Garden Green, Brilliant Blue, and Confetti White card stock; Basic Black, Brilliant Blue, Brocade Blue, More Mustard, and Garden Green Classic pads; watercolor brush; Blue hemp; needle

68 A
Snowflakes set; Confetti White, Brocade Blue, and Night of Navy card stock; VersaMark pad; Silver Encore! pad; Night of Navy Classic pad; Crystal Clear embossing powder; stamping sponge; Stampin' Dimensionals; Navy wide organdy ribbon; Silver metallic ribbon

68 B
Snowy Play and Little Shapes sets; Brilliant Blue, Ballet Blue, Eggplant Envy, and Confetti White card stock; Eggplant Envy, Basic Black, Going Gray, Creamy Caramel, Forest Foliage, Only Orange, Brilliant Blue, Not Quite Navy, and Close to Cocoa Classic pads; watercolor brush; Blue hemp; needle

68 C
Snowy Play and All-Year Cheer I sets; Not Quite Navy, Eggplant Envy, Confetti White, Ballet Blue, and Brilliant Blue card stock; Basic Black, Night of Navy, Not Quite Navy, Ballet Blue, Eggplant Envy, Bordering Blue, Going Gray, Chocolate Chip, Only Orange, and Tempting Turquoise Classic pads; watercolor brush; Stampin' Dimensionals; Bordering Blue eyelets; Naturals hemp; 1/16" Circle punch; Snowflakes brass template

69 A
Holiday Print background stamp; Not Quite Navy, Night of Navy, Brushed Silver, Ultrasmooth White, and Radiant White vellum card stock; Night of Navy, Brocade Blue, and Not Quite Navy Classic pads; stipple brushes; Silver metallic ribbon

69 B
The Gift of Love set; Holiday Print background stamp; Ballet Blue, Brocade Blue, Bordering Blue, and Confetti White card stock; Basic Black, Blush Blossom, Creamy Caramel, Going Gray, Mellow Moss, Night of Navy, and Ballet Blue Classic pads; watercolor brush; Southwest Corner punch; crochet thread; button

69 C
The Gift of Love set; Not Quite Navy, Confetti White, and More Mustard card stock; Basic Black, Eggplant Envy, Not Quite Navy, Creamy Caramel, More Mustard, Blush Blossom, Bordering Blue, Going Gray, Chocolate Chip, Bliss Blue, and Night of Navy Classic pads; watercolor brush; crochet thread; needle

70 A
Sketch It set; Old Olive, Ultrasmooth White, More Mustard, and Ruby Red card stock; Summer Sun, Old Olive, and Ruby Red Classic pads; Stampin' Dimensionals; Gold and Natural hemp; twig; sewing machine and thread; needle; button; crochet thread

70 B
Sketch It set; Confetti White, Ruby Red, and Old Olive card stock; Old Olive and Ruby Red Classic pads; VersaMark pad; Top Boss pad; Stampin' Pastels; Gold Glory embossing powder; watercolor brush; Gold metallic ribbon; Stampin' Dimensionals

70 C
Sketch It set; Ruby Red, Confetti White, and Radiant White vellum card stock; Confetti White tag sheet; Ruby Red Classic pad; White Craft pad; Stampin' Dimensional; White eyelets; White narrow organdy ribbon; string

70 D
Sketch It and All-Year Cheer I sets; By Definition background stamp; Creamy Caramel, Old Olive, Radiant White vellum, and Ultrasmooth White card stock; Summer Sun, Old Olive, and Creamy Caramel Classic pads; Jumbo, 1/2", and 1/16" Circle punches; Creamy Caramel, More Mustard, and Really Rust eyelets; Stampin' Dimensionals; raffia; Natural hemp

72 A
Sun-Ripened, Classic Caps, and Fun Phrases sets; Hand-Stitched background stamp; Really Rust, Old Olive, More Mustard, and Confetti Ivory card stock; Olive Green mulberry paper; Basic Black, Really Rust, Old Olive, More Mustard, Garden Green, and Close to Cocoa Classic pads; Old Olive and Really Rust Craft pads; watercolor brush; Silver Mini Deco Fasteners; Stampin' Dimensionals; 26-gauge Wire Works

72 B
Autumn set; Confetti Cream, Really Rust, and Old Olive card stock; Old Olive and Really Rust Classic pads; skeleton leaf; Really Rust eyelets; Stampin' Dimensionals; watercolor brush; jute; needle; twig; button

73 A
Sun-Ripened II, Itty Bitty Backgrounds, and All-Year Cheer I sets; Creamy Caramel, Ultrasmooth Vanilla, Old Olive, and Really Rust card stock; Basic Black, Old Olive, Creamy Caramel, Ruby Red, Really Rust, Old Olive, Garden Green, and Summer Sun Classic pads; VersaMark pad; watercolor brush; Stampin' Dimensionals; raffia; 1/16" Circle punch; crochet thread

73 B
Changing Seasons and Many Thanks sets; Just Jeans background stamp; Confetti White, Old Olive, Creamy Caramel, and Really Rust card stock; Basic Black, Bordering Blue, Old Olive, Garden Green, Going Gray, More Mustard, Really Rust, Eggplant Envy, Close to Cocoa, and Chocolate Chip Classic pads; Really Rust Craft pad; watercolor brush; Really Rust eyelets; Natural hemp; Stampin' Dimensionals

74 A
Lovely as a Tree, Little Shapes, Itty Bitty Backgrounds, and Classic Alphabet sets; French Script background stamp; More Mustard, Ruby Red, Confetti Cream, Old Olive, and Creamy Caramel card stock; More Mustard, Old Olive, and Ruby Red Classic pads; 1/2" Circle punch; skeleton leaves; Old Olive eyelet; Natural hemp

74 B
Pinecones and Classic Alphabet sets; Close to Cocoa, Confetti Cream, and Radiant White vellum card stock; Tudor Designer Series vellum; Chocolate Chip and Close to Cocoa Classic pads; sponge brayer; font CD; crochet thread; needle; buttons

74 C
Pinecones and All-Year Cheer I sets; Old Olive, Ruby Red, Creamy Caramel, and Confetti Cream card stock; Ruby Red and Old Olive Classic pads; VersaMark pad; Stampin' Pastels; Stampin' Dimensionals; Natural hemp; Southwest Corner punch; watercolor brush

75 A
Etruscan and All-Year Cheer I sets; Ruby Red, Old Olive, Confetti Cream, and Close to Cocoa card stock; Ruby Red, Old Olive, and Close to Cocoa Classic pads; Close to Cocoa, Ruby Red, and Old Olive markers; watercolor brush; Old Olive eyelet; Cream grosgrain ribbon; button; crochet thread

75 B
Etruscan set; Old Olive, Ruby Red, Creamy Caramel, and Confetti Cream card stock; Old Olive Classic pad; crochet thread; buttons; needle

75 C
Country Pleasures and All-Year Cheer III sets; Old Olive, Creamy Caramel, Ruby Red, and Confetti Cream card stock; Basic Black, Only Orange, Really Rust, Ruby Red, Brocade Blue, Old Olive, and Garden Green Classic pads; watercolor brush; Stampin' Dimensionals; Natural hemp

75 D
Country Pleasures and God Bless sets; Stipple Plaid background stamp; Creamy Caramel, Ruby Red, Garden Green, Close to Cocoa, and Confetti Cream card stock; Basic Black, Close to Cocoa, Bordering Blue, Garden Green, and Creamy Caramel Classic pads; watercolor brush; Stampin' Dimensionals; Natural hemp; 1/16" Circle punch; button

76 A
Something Nice set; Ballet Blue, Barely Banana, Ultrasmooth White, and Rose Red card stock; Basic Black and Rose Red Classic pads

76 B
Thank You Blocks and Bold Alphabet sets; Barely Banana, Rose Romance, and Chocolate Chip card stock; Chocolate Chip Craft pad; journaling marker; Stampin' Pastels; Close to Cocoa square eyelets; Natural hemp

77 A
Bold Basics, Little Shapes, and Simple Sayings II sets; Ballet Blue, Rose Romance, and Ultrasmooth White card stock; Barely Banana, Ballet Blue, and Rose Romance Classic pads; Bold Basics brass template; 1/16" Circle punch; Natural hemp

77 B
Bold Basics set; Ultrasmooth White and Ballet Blue card stock; Barely Banana party favor box; Rose Romance Classic pad; Folk Heart punch; 22-gauge Wire Works; Silver star eyelets; Bold Basics brass template

77 C
Little Layers II, Itty Bitty Backgrounds, and Simple Sayings II sets; Chocolate Chip, Barely Banana, and Ultrasmooth White card stock; Chocolate Chip Classic pad; crochet thread; needle

77 D
Little Layers II and Fun Phrases sets; Ballet Blue, Rose Romance, and Ultrasmooth White card stock; Ballet Blue and Rose Romance Classic pads; crochet thread; needle

78 A
Favorite Teddy Bear set; Rose Red, Naturals White, Chocolate Chip, Creamy Caramel, and Radiant White vellum card stock; Basic Black, Really Rust, Creamy Caramel, and Rose Red Classic pads; White Craft pad; VersaMark pad; watercolor brush; Stampin' Dimensionals

78 B
Favorite Teddy Bear set; Naturals White, Brocade Blue, and Rose Red card stock; Basic Black, Creamy Caramel, Chocolate Chip, Rose Red, Barely Banana, and Going Gray card stock; Stampin' Dimensionals; watercolor brush

79 A
Tags & More set; Soft Swirls background stamp; Rose Red, Confetti White, and Mellow Moss card stock; Confetti White stationery box; Basic Black and Rose Red Classic pads; Rose Red and Mellow Moss markers; Stampin' Dimensionals; White narrow organdy ribbon

79 B
Tree for All Seasons and Simple Sayings sets; Not Quite Navy, Confetti White, Rose Red, Barely Banana, and Old Olive card stock; square envelope; Basic Black, Old Olive, Garden Green, Barely Banana, Rose Red, Not Quite Navy, Bliss Blue, Creamy Caramel, More Mustard, and Brocade Blue Classic pads; watercolor brush; Old Olive eyelets

79 C
Little Somethings and Birthday Greetings sets; Pindot wheel; Naturals White, Rose Red, and Creamy Caramel card stock; Basic Black, Rose Red, Old Olive, Brocade Blue, Close to Cocoa, Pretty in Pink, Creamy Caramel, and Barely Banana Classic pads; Basic Black cartridge; watercolor brush; Stampin' Dimensionals; Pretty in Pink eyelet; French Blue grosgrain ribbon

80 A
Watercolor Fun set; Swirls background stamp; Taken with Teal, Ruby Red, Radiant White vellum, and Ultrasmooth White card stock; Taken with Teal and Ruby Red Classic pads; Taken with Teal, Not Quite Navy, Ruby Red, and Yoyo Yellow markers; Real Red eyelets

80 B
Watercolor Fun set; Green Galore, Gable Green, Taken with Teal, Yoyo Yellow, and Ultrasmooth White card stock; Green Galore and Taken with Teal Classic pads; Yoyo Yellow and Green Galore eyelets; needle

80 C
Bitty Bolds and All-Year Cheer III sets; Bold Blocks wheel; Green Galore, Gable Green, Taken with Teal, and Ultrasmooth White card stock; Ruby Red Classic pad; White Craft pad; Taken with Teal cartridge; White eyelets

80 D
Bitty Bolds and All-Year Cheer I sets; Ruby Red and Ultrasmooth White card stock; Ruby Red Classic pad; White Craft pad; Ruby Red marker; air art tool; Silver eyelet; Silver metallic cord; 22-gauge Wire Works; embroidery floss; needle

81 A
Tropical Blossoms and All-Year Cheer I sets; Ruby Red, Yoyo Yellow, and Ultrasmooth White card stock; Ruby Red, Gable Green, and Yoyo Yellow Classic pads; 1/16" and 1/8" Circle punches; Gold hemp

81 B
Fresh Flowers and All-Year Cheer III sets; Blossoms & Bugs wheel; Confetti White, Taken with Teal, and Ruby Red card stock; Ruby Red and Taken with Teal Classic pads; Ruby Red cartridge; Stampin' Dimensionals; Red grosgrain ribbon

81 C
Fresh Flowers and All-Year Cheer I sets; Yoyo Yellow, Ultrasmooth White, Green Galore, and Taken with Teal card stock; Taken with Teal, Yoyo Yellow, Green Galore, and Gable Green Classic pads; watercolor brush; White eyelet; 22- and 26-gauge Wire Works

82 A
Watercolor Garden and All-Year Cheer I sets; Hand-Stitched background stamp; Bordering Blue, Barely Banana, and Naturals Ivory card stock; Mellow Moss, Bliss Blue, Barely Banana, and Brocade Blue Classic pads; VersaMark pad; watercolor brush; Cream grosgrain ribbon; Stampin' Dimensional

82 B
Watercolor Garden set; Naturals Ivory, Barely Banana, and Ruby Red card stock; Ruby Red, Close to Cocoa, Mellow Moss, Old Olive, and Barely Banana Classic pads; Ruby Red and Chocolate Chip markers; watercolor brush; Cream grosgrain ribbon; button; embroidery thread

82 C
Watercolor Minis and All-Year Cheer I sets; Filigree background stamp; Naturals Ivory, Ruby Red, and Bordering Blue card stock; VersaMark pad; Barely Banana, Ruby Red, Mellow Moss, Old Olive, Bordering Blue, and Brocade Blue Classic pads; Rectangle punch; French Blue grosgrain ribbon

82 D
Watercolor Minis set; Naturals Ivory, Barely Banana, and Ruby Red card stock; Barely Banana, Mellow Moss, and Ruby Red Classic pads; Barely Banana small flower eyelets; Cream grosgrain ribbon; Stampin' Dimensionals; buttons; embroidery thread

83 A
Roses in Winter and Simple Sayings sets; Ruby Red, Brocade Blue, and Ultrasmooth Vanilla card stock; Swirl printed vellum; Cameo Coral, Ruby Red, Bordering Blue, and Mellow Moss Classic pads; Spring Moss grosgrain ribbon; Stampin' Dimensionals

84 A
Botanicals set; Confetti Cream, Garden Green, and More Mustard card stock; Basic Black, More Mustard, and Garden Green Classic pads; watercolor brush; skeleton leaves; Natural hemp; Maple Leaf punch; 1/16" Circle punch; Stampin' Dimensionals; twig; buttons; crochet thread

84 B
Botanicals and All-Year Cheer II sets; Confetti Cream and More Mustard card stock; Ruby Red trapezoid box; Ruby Red Classic pad; Stampin' Dimensionals; 1/16" and 1/8" Circle punches; Regal Tones fiber; crochet thread

84 C
Botanicals set; Confetti Cream, Confetti Tan, Garden Green, Ruby Red, and More Mustard card stock; Red mulberry paper; Basic Black and Creamy Caramel Classic pads; Ruby Red, Garden Green, and More Mustard Craft pads; watercolor brush; Ruby Red square eyelet; Silver Mini Deco Fasteners; Earth Tones fiber; Natural hemp; Stampin' Dimensionals; staple; button

84 D
Botanicals set; More Mustard and Ruby Red card stock; Basic Black, Creamy Caramel, More Mustard, Ruby Red, and Garden Green Classic pads; watercolor brushes; Regal Tones fiber; bleach

85 A
Vine & Berry, Many Thanks, and Itty Bitty Backgrounds sets; Confetti Cream, Mellow Moss, Garden Green, and Ruby Red card stock; Garden Green and Ruby Red Classic pads; Stampin' Dimensionals; Ruby Red square eyelet; Natural hemp; needle

86 A
Fanciful Flowers and All-Year Cheer I sets; Positively Pink, Barely Banana, Cameo Coral, and Confetti Cream card stock; Candy Designer Series vellum; Cameo Coral, Pretty in Pink, and Mellow Moss Classic pads; Stampin' Dimensionals; Cream grosgrain ribbon; Envelope Template Assortment I; crochet thread; button

86 B
Terrific Tulips and Classic Alphabet sets; Naturals Ivory, Mellow Moss, Garden Green, and Positively Pink card stock; Rose Romance, Positively Pink, Pretty in Pink, Mellow Moss, and Barely Banana Craft pads; Pretty in Pink eyelet; Ivory narrow organdy ribbon; Stampin' Dimensionals; embroidery floss; button

86 C
Terrific Tulips and Simple Sayings sets; Cameo Coral, Mellow Moss, and Naturals Ivory card stock; Mellow Moss and Cameo Coral Classic pads; Spring Moss grosgrain ribbon

87 A
Daisy and Simple Sayings II sets; Barely Banana, Naturals Ivory, Mellow Moss, Radiant White vellum, and Cameo Coral card stock; Cameo Coral and Mellow Moss Classic pads; Stampin' Dimensionals; crochet thread; needle; button

87 B
Daisy, Little Shapes, and Simple Sayings II sets; Dots & Daisies wheel; Barely Banana, Naturals White, and Mellow Moss card stock; Barely Banana and Mellow Moss Classic pads; Barely Banana cartridge; Stampin' Dimensionals; Gold Mini Deco Fasteners; Olive Green wide organdy ribbon; Stampin' Dimensionals

88 A
Hand-Painted Petites and Classic Alphabet sets; French Script background stamp; Mellow Moss, Confetti Cream, Ultrasmooth Vanilla, and Rose Romance card stock; Rose Red, Rose Romance, Creamy Caramel, Old Olive, Mellow Moss, and Summer Sun Classic pads; 1/8" Circle punch; Natural hemp

88 B
Early Spring set; French Script background stamp; Ultrasmooth Vanilla card stock; Burgundy mulberry paper; More Mustard pouch box; VersaMark pad; Baroque Burgundy Classic pad; Stampin' Pastels; Gold wide organdy ribbon

89 A
Classic Alphabet set; Elegant Rose stamp; Mellow Moss and Ultrasmooth Vanilla card stock; Burgundy mulberry paper; Burgundy, Mellow Moss, and Creamy Caramel Classic pads; VersaMark pad; watercolor brush; Gold Mini Deco Fasteners; Stampin' Pastels; stamping sponges; 1/8" Circle punch; Natural hemp; beads; notebook

89 B
Stipple Rose stamp; Baroque Burgundy and Creamy Caramel card stock; Burgundy mulberry paper; Baroque Burgundy, Old Olive, and Garden Green Classic pads; VersaMark pad; watercolor brush; Black detail embossing powder; Burgundy wide organdy ribbon; Stampin' Dimensionals

89 C
Stipple Hydrangea stamp; Mellow Moss, Mauve Mist, and Ultrasmooth Vanilla card stock; Celery mulberry paper; metallic pencils; 1/16" Circle punch; Gold metallic cord

90 A
Bitty Bouquets and All-Year Cheer I sets; Swirls & Blossoms background stamp; Rose Red, Gable Green, Barely Banana, and Confetti White card stock; Basic Black and Rose Red Classic pads; Stampin' Pastels; Stampin' Dimensionals; Green Galore and Yoyo Yellow eyelets; Yoyo Yellow and Positively Pink large flower eyelets; White grosgrain ribbon

90 B
Simply Spring and Simple Sayings II sets; Pretty Paisley background stamp; Lavender Lace, Barely Banana, and Mellow Moss card stock; Lavender Lace Classic pad; VersaMark pad; Stampin' Pastels; Cream grosgrain ribbon; Stampin' Dimensionals; Simply Spring brass template

90 C
Simply Spring and Brushstroke Alphabet sets; Busy Bees wheel; Ultrasmooth Vanilla, Mellow Moss, and Barely Banana card stock; Basic Black Classic pad; Black cartridge; Summer Sun marker; 1/4" Circle punch; Cream grosgrain ribbon; Stampin' Dimensionals

91 A
Springtime Fun and All-Year Cheer II sets; Lavender Lace, Ultrasmooth Vanilla, Only Orange, Rose Romance, Barely Banana, and Gable Green card stock; Only Orange, Gable Green, Lavender Lace, Barely Banana, and Rose Romance markers; Only Orange, Positively Pink, Yoyo Yellow, and Green Galore eyelets

92 A
Flower of the Month and Happy Birthday Frame sets; Mint Melody, Perfect Plum, and Confetti White card stock; Basic Black, Mint Melody, Barely Banana, and Perfect Plum Classic pads; watercolor brush; White mulberry paper; 1/8" Circle punch; Light Green narrow organdy ribbon

92 B
Flower of the Month and Happy Birthday Frame sets; Perfect Plum, Confetti White, and Barely Banana card stock; Celery mulberry paper; Basic Black, Perfect Plum, and Gable Green Classic pads; White Craft pad; watercolor brush; 1/8" Circle punch; White narrow organdy ribbon; button

93 A
Watercolor Garden II and Brushstroke Alphabet sets; Bliss Blue, Perfect Plum, and Barely Banana card stock; Perfect Plum, Barely Banana, Mint Melody, Bliss Blue, and Mauve Mist Craft pads; journaling marker; bleach

93 B
Watercolor Garden II and All-Year Cheer III sets; Confetti White and Bliss Blue card stock; Splash Designer Series vellum; Confetti White tag sheet; Perfect Plum, Bliss Blue, Mauve Mist, Mint Melody, and Barely Banana Classic pads; stamping sponge; 1/8" Circle punch; Blue narrow organdy ribbon

93 C
Spring Garden set; Perfect Plum, Mint Melody, and Confetti White card stock; Confetti White tag sheet; Mint Melody, Sage Shadow, and Perfect Plum Classic pads; Perfect Plum eyelets; Light Green narrow grosgrain ribbon

94 A
Perfect Petals and All-Year Cheer I sets; Antique background stamp; Lovely Lilac, Confetti White, and Almost Amethyst card stock; Lovely Lilac Classic pad; VersaMark pad; Stampin' Pastels; White and Purple mulberry paper; Stampin' Dimensionals; Lovely Lilac large flower eyelet; Brights fiber

94 B
Perfect Petals and All-Year Cheer II sets; By Definition background stamp; Confetti White, Sage Shadow, and Radiant White vellum card stock; Sage Shadow Classic pad; VersaMark pad; Stampin' Pastels; Sage Shadow eyelets; Light Green narrow organdy ribbon; Silver metallic cord; spray fixative

94 C
Simple Florals and All-Year Cheer III sets; By Definition background stamp; Confetti White, Rose Romance, Pretty in Pink, and Sage Shadow card stock; Basic Black, Rose Romance, Sage Shadow, and Going Gray Classic pads; watercolor brush; Stampin' Dimensionals; Silver metallic cord; Pretty in Pink heart eyelet

94 D
Simple Florals and Simple Sayings sets; Filigree background stamp; Confetti White, Barely Banana, Sage Shadow, and Radiant White vellum card stock; More Mustard Classic pad; Sage Shadow Craft pad; VersaMark pad; Stampin' Pastels; Barely Banana small flower eyelets; Sage Shadow eyelets; Ivory narrow organdy ribbon

95 A
Seeds of Kindness set; Dandelions wheel; Ultrasmooth White, Barely Banana, and Sage Shadow card stock; Sage Shadow, Barely Banana, and Summer Sun Classic pads; Sage Shadow cartridge; Sage Shadow eyelets; Natural hemp; Stampin' Dimensionals

96 A
Sweet Flowers set; Antique background stamp; Old Olive, Ultrasmooth Vanilla, and Ruby Red card stock; Basic Black, Ruby Red, Old Olive, Chocolate Chip, Mellow Moss, Summer Sun, and Really Rust Classic pads; watercolor brush; Stampin' Dimensionals; 1/16" Circle punch; Gold metallic cord; Olive Green wide organdy ribbon

96 B
Sweet Flowers and All-Year Cheer I sets; Ultrasmooth Vanilla card stock; Ruby Red favor box; Basic Black, Ruby Red, Summer Sun, and Old Olive Classic pads; watercolor brush; 1/16" and 1/8" Circle punches; Ivory narrow organdy ribbon; Gold metallic cord

96 C
Feathered Hope set; Barely Banana, Mellow Moss, and Ultrasmooth Vanilla card stock; Barely Banana and Mellow Moss tag sheets; Basic Black, Mellow Moss, Ruby Red, Creamy Caramel, Forest Foliage, Old Olive, Really Rust, Chocolate Chip, Barely Banana, and Going Gray Classic pads; watercolor brush; Barely Banana eyelet; Natural hemp; crochet thread

96 D
Feathered Hope and Hope for Comfort sets; Ultrasmooth Vanilla, Really Rust, and Mellow Moss card stock; Olive Green mulberry paper; Going Gray, Mellow Moss, Barely Banana, Old Olive, Really Rust, and Creamy Caramel Classic pads; watercolor brush; 1/16" Circle punch; twig; crochet thread

97 A
Lovely Leaves set; Really Rust and Ultrasmooth Vanilla card stock; Olive Green mulberry paper; Pumpkin Patch Spectrum pad; Really Rust Classic pad

97 B
Ferns and Bold & Basic Greetings sets; Really Rust, Barely Banana, and Old Olive card stock; Really Rust Classic pad; 1/8" Circle punch; Natural hemp; bleach

99 A
Heart Blossoms and All-Year Cheer I sets; Marvelous Magenta, Old Olive, and Ultrasmooth Vanilla card stock; Basic Black, Old Olive, Lovely Lilac, Garden Green, Marvelous Magenta, Almost Amethyst, and Close to Cocoa Classic pads; watercolor brushes; Blue narrow organdy ribbon; Silver Mini Deco Fasteners

99 B
Heart Blossoms set; Harlequin background stamp; Marvelous Magenta, Old Olive, Mellow Moss, and Ultrasmooth Vanilla card stock; Celery mulberry paper; Basic Black, Marvelous Magenta, Old Olive, and Chocolate Chip Classic pads; watercolor brush; Silver Mini Deco Fasteners; Silver metallic cord

99 C
Delightful Doodles and All-Year Cheer III sets; Ultrasmooth Vanilla, Eggplant Envy, Summer Sun, and Old Olive card stock; Ultrasmooth Vanilla tag sheet; Old Olive and Eggplant Envy Classic pads; Summer Sun and Eggplant Envy markers; white round metal edge tag; paper crimper; Old Olive eyelets; Silver large circle eyelet; 1/16" Circle punch; Gold hemp; Yellow Gold grosgrain ribbon; Stampin' Dimensionals; button; string

99 D
Delightful Doodles, Itty Bitty Backgrounds, and All-Year Cheer III sets; Old Olive, More Mustard, Really Rust, Eggplant Envy, and Confetti White card stock; Old Olive, More Mustard, Really Rust, and Eggplant Envy Classic pads; More Mustard square eyelets; Natural hemp; Stampin' Dimensionals; sewing machine and thread

100 A
Smile set; Lovely Lilac, Summer Sun, Real Red, and Ultrasmooth White card stock; Summer Sun, Real Red, and Lovely Lilac Classic pads; Real Red eyelets; Stampin' Dimensionals

100 B
Smile and Smile Accessories sets; Real Red, Lovely Lilac, Old Olive, Summer Sun, and Ultrasmooth White card stock; Lovely Lilac, Old Olive, Real Red, and Summer Sun Classic pads; Stampin' Dimensionals; Lovely Lilac eyelets

100 C
Scribbles and Simple Sayings II sets; Real Red, Summer Sun, Old Olive, and Ultrasmooth White card stock; Summer Sun, Real Red, and Old Olive Classic pads; Summer Sun star eyelets; needle; sewing machine and thread

101 A
Good Times set; Real Red, Lovely Lilac, Old Olive, Summer Sun, and Ultrasmooth White card stock; Lovely Lilac, Basic Black, Real Red, and Summer Sun Classic pads; watercolor brush; 26-gauge Wire Works; beads

101 B
Good Times and Beyond the Basics sets; Lovely Lilac, Real Red, and Ultrasmooth White card stock; Lovely Lilac and Real Red tag sheets; Real Red, Basic Black, and Lovely Lilac Classic pads; watercolor brush; Real Red and Lovely Lilac eyelets; Stampin' Dimensionals; Black hemp; Delphinium grosgrain ribbon; sewing machine and thread; beads

101 C
Good Times set; Confetti White card stock; Real Red and Old Olive tag sheets; Basic Black, Old Olive, Summer Sun, Chocolate Chip, and Going Gray Classic pads; watercolor brush; 1/8" Circle punch; Red grosgrain ribbon; Old Olive oval eyelet; crochet thread; button

101 D
Fanciful Favorites set; Confetti White, Real Red, Basic Black, Old Olive, and Summer Sun card stock; Basic Black, Old Olive, Real Red, and Summer Sun Classic pads; Old Olive, Real Red, and Black eyelets; Stampin' Dimensionals; sewing machine and thread

101 E
Fanciful Favorites set; Swirls & Blossoms background stamp; Confetti White, Lovely Lilac, and Real Red card stock; Lovely Lilac, Real Red, and Summer Sun Classic pads; Stampin' Dimensionals; Yellow Gold grosgrain ribbon; 1/16" Circle punch; watercolor brush; Gold hemp

102 A
Nice & Easy Notes; Confetti Tan, Confetti Cream, Baroque Burgundy, and Ultrasmooth Vanilla card stock; Basic Black, Old Olive, Garden Green, Baroque Burgundy, Only Orange, More Mustard, and Chocolate Chip Classic pads; watercolor brush; Stampin' Dimensionals; 1/8" Circle punch; raffia; sewing machine and thread

102 B
Nice & Easy Notes set; Confetti White and Gable Green card stock; Basic Black, Gable Green, Going Gray, and Real Red Classic pads; watercolor brush

102 C
Nice & Easy Notes set; Real Red, Ultrasmooth White, and Gable Green card stock; Basic Black and Really Rust Classic pads; Real Red, Gable Green, Green Galore, and More Mustard markers; air art tool; watercolor brush; Green Galore eyelets; Red grosgrain ribbon

103 A
Darling Dragons and Beyond the Basics sets; Gable Green, Ultrasmooth White, Yoyo Yellow, and Brilliant Blue card stock; Gable Green, Basic Black, Brilliant Blue, and Yoyo Yellow Classic pads; watercolor brush; Yoyo Yellow, White, Green Galore, and Brilliant Blue eyelets; 26-gauge Wire Works

103 B
Darling Dragons and Beyond the Basics sets; Ultrasmooth White and Gable Green card stock; Basic Black, Green Galore, Gable Green, Real Red, and Yoyo Yellow Classic pads; watercolor brush; Green Galore eyelets; Crystal Effects

103 C
A Greeting for All Reasons and All-Year Cheer I sets; French Script background stamp; Real Red, Creamy Caramel, and Confetti White card stock; Red mulberry paper; Basic Black, Real Red, and Creamy Caramel Classic pads; watercolor brush; stamping sponge; Real Red eyelet; Gold Mini Deco Fastener; 1/16" Circle punch; Natural hemp; 26-gauge Wire Works; Red grosgrain ribbon

103 D
A Greeting for All Reasons set; Ultrasmooth White, Real Red, Garden Green, and Gable Green card stock; Garden Green, Gable Green, and Real Red Classic pads; Stampin' Dimensionals; Red grosgrain ribbon; 1/8" Circle punch

104 A
Handmade with Love set; Mellow Moss and Ultrasmooth Vanilla card stock; Basic Black, Eggplant Envy, Going Gray, More Mustard, and Mellow Moss Classic pads; watercolor brush

104 B
Handmade with Love set; Eggplant Envy, Creamy Caramel, and Ultrasmooth Vanilla card stock; Ultrasmooth Vanilla tag sheet; Eggplant Envy Classic pad; Creamy Caramel eyelets; Natural hemp

104 C
Handmade with Love II set; Bordering Blue and Ultrasmooth Vanilla card stock; Bordering Blue Classic pad; Eggplant Envy marker

104 D
Simple Wishes, Little Shapes, and All-Year Cheer I sets; Bordering Blue, Eggplant Envy, Barely Banana, and Ultrasmooth Vanilla card stock; Bordering Blue, Basic Black, Eggplant Envy, Mellow Moss, Creamy Caramel, and Barely Banana Classic pads; Stampin' Dimensionals; 1/16" Circle punch; Cream grosgrain ribbon; crochet thread

105 A
Simple Sketches set; Filigree background stamp; Creamy Caramel, Eggplant Envy, Mellow Moss, and Ultrasmooth Vanilla card stock; VersaMark pad; Eggplant Envy Classic pad; Stampin' Pastels; stamping sponges; 1/16" Circle punch; Natural hemp; Stampin' Dimensionals; twig

105 B
Simply Sweet set; Happy Birthday Greetings background stamp; Mellow Moss, Eggplant Envy, Barely Banana, and Confetti Cream card stock; Basic Black, Mellow Moss, Bordering Blue, Barely Banana, and Eggplant Envy Classic pads; watercolor brush; crochet thread; button

105 C
Simply Sweet and Simple Sayings II sets; Harlequin background stamp; Bordering Blue, Eggplant Envy, and Confetti Cream card stock; Basic Black, Mellow Moss, Creamy Caramel, Eggplant Envy, and Bordering Blue Classic pads; watercolor brush; Vanilla oval eyelets; Natural hemp

106 A
Business Memos set; Brilliant Blue, Ultrasmooth White, Green Galore, and Tempting Turquoise card stock; Basic Black Classic pad; Tempting Turquoise, Green Galore, Positively Pink, Yoyo Yellow, and Brilliant Blue markers; Turquoise grosgrain ribbon; Green Galore triangle eyelet

106 B
Business Memos set; Real Red, Brilliant Blue, Tempting Turquoise, and Confetti White card stock; Brilliant Blue, Taken with Teal, and Real Red Classic pads; watercolor brush; Brilliant Blue eyelets

106 C
Hang in There set; Green Galore, Real Red, and Confetti White card stock; Basic Black Classic pad; Tempting Turquoise, Yoyo Yellow, and Gable Green markers; 1/8" Circle punch; Red grosgrain ribbon

107 A
Vivid Greetings set; Confetti White, Green Galore, Real Red, and Brilliant Blue card stock; White Craft pad; Real Red, Brilliant Blue, and Green Galore Classic pads; watercolor brush; Winter White embossing powder; Stampin' Dimensionals; 1/16" Circle punch; 22-gauge Wire Works

107 B
Vivid Greetings set; Brilliant Blue, Real Red, Tempting Turquoise, Green Galore, and Ultrasmooth White card stock; Brilliant Blue Classic pad; Tempting Turquoise and Green Galore triangle eyelets; Stampin' Dimensionals

107 C
Vertical Greetings set; Stipple Plaid background stamp; Tempting Turquoise, Brilliant Blue, and Green Galore card stock; Tempting Turquoise Classic pad; White Craft pad; Tempting Turquoise triangle eyelet; Green Galore eyelets; white string

108 A

Groovy, Alphabet Fun Upper, and Alphabet Fun Lower sets; Flower Power wheel; Gable Green, Ultrasmooth White, Radiant White vellum, and Brilliant Blue card stock; Ultrasmooth White tag sheets; Brilliant Blue, Yoyo Yellow, and Gable Green Craft pads; Brilliant Blue cartridge; journaling marker; blender pens; Green Galore eyelets; 26-gauge Wire Works; 1/16" Circle punch; beads

108 B

Groovy set; Gable Green, Brilliant Blue, and Ultrasmooth White card stock; Brilliant Blue, Green Galore, and Gable Green Classic pads; White Craft pad; Green Galore eyelets; Blue hemp; Stampin' Dimensionals; Royal grosgrain ribbon; Envelope Template Assortment I

109 A

Mini Mates set; Green Galore and Confetti White card stock; Confetti White and Real Red tag sheets; Real Red Classic pad; Barely Banana, Gable Green, and Real Red markers; watercolor brush; Red grosgrain ribbon; Silver Mini Deco Fasteners; White narrow organdy ribbon; thread; bleach

109 B

Mini Mates set; Real Red, Brilliant Blue, and Confetti White card stock; Confetti White and Brilliant Blue tag sheets; Real Red and Basic Black Classic pads; 1/8" Circle punch; Silver Mini Deco Fastener; Blue hemp; crochet thread; needle

109 C

Mini Mates set; Green Galore and Radiant White vellum card stock; Brilliant Blue and Ultrasmooth White tag sheets; VersaMark pad; Brilliant Blue Classic pad; Sterling Silver embossing powder; watercolor brush; Silver metallic cord; White narrow organdy ribbon; Brilliant Blue eyelets

109 D

Mini Mates and Brushstroke Alphabet sets; Night of Navy, Confetti Tan, Real Red, and Ultrasmooth Vanilla card stock; Real Red and Night of Navy Classic pads; watercolor brush; 1/16" Circle punch; Stampin' Dimensionals; 26-gauge Wire Works

109 E

Happy Healing set; Real Red, Yoyo Yellow, Brilliant Blue, and Ultrasmooth White card stock; Basic Black, Real Red, Yoyo Yellow, and Bliss Blue Classic pads; watercolor brush; Stampin' Dimensionals; 1/8" Circle punch; Gold hemp; Royal grosgrain ribbon

110 A

Feathered Friends set; Hand-Stitched background stamp; Creamy Caramel, Real Red, and Confetti White card stock; Creamy Caramel, Basic Black, Real Red, Not Quite Navy, Chocolate Chip, Garden Green, and Bordering Blue Classic pads; watercolor brush; Stampin' Dimensionals; crochet thread; needle; button

110 B

I Love You and Itty Bitty Backgrounds sets; Real Red and Creamy Caramel card stock; VersaMark pad; Black embossing powder; Ivory narrow organdy ribbon; paper crimper; crochet thread; needle; bleach

111 A

Nice & Narrow set; Not Quite Navy, Real Red, Mellow Moss, Barely Banana, and Confetti White card stock; Basic Black and Not Quite Navy Classic pads; White Craft pad; Mellow Moss marker; White eyelet; 26-gauge Wire Works; needle

111 B

Nice & Narrow and Fun Phrases sets; Real Red, Ultrasmooth White, Radiant White vellum, and Mellow Moss card stock; Basic Black and Real Red Classic pads; White Craft pad; Real Red and White eyelets; Stampin' Dimensionals

111 C

Quick & Cute and Simple Sayings II sets; Real Red, Barely Banana, and Confetti White card stock; Real Red and Barely Banana Classic pads; watercolor brush; 26-gauge Wire Works; Stampin' Dimensionals; Real Red large flower eyelet; Barely Banana eyelet; Red grosgrain ribbon

111 D

Quick & Cute and Background Basics sets; Not Quite Navy, Radiant White vellum, and Barely Banana card stock; White Craft pad; Not Quite Navy Classic pad; Silver star eyelets; Silver Mini Deco Fasteners; Stampin' Dimensionals; 1/16" Circle punch; Silver metallic cord

112 A

Many Moos and Fun Phrases sets; Swirls background stamp; Ruby Red, Old Olive, Not Quite Navy, and Confetti White card stock; Basic Black, Going Gray, Creamy Caramel, Old Olive, Ruby Red, Not Quite Navy, More Mustard, and Bordering Blue Classic pads; watercolor brush; Stampin' Dimensionals; 22-gauge Wire Works

112 B

Many Moos, Classic Alphabet, and All-Year Cheer II sets; Filigree background stamp; Ruby Red, Confetti White, and Basic Black card stock; Basic Black, Ruby Red, Barely Banana, Eggplant Envy, and Creamy Caramel Classic pads; watercolor brush; Stampin' Dimensionals; Black grosgrain ribbon; Black eyelet; Black hemp; Hearts & Stars template

112 C

Teddy & Friends and Simple Sayings sets; Stipple Plaid background stamp; Old Olive, Not Quite Navy, and Confetti White card stock; Old Olive, Basic Black, Creamy Caramel, Really Red, and Close to Cocoa Classic pads; watercolor brush; Olive Green wide organdy ribbon

113 A

Coast to Coast and All-Year Cheer II sets; Not Quite Navy, Confetti White, and Bordering Blue card stock; Basic Black, Real Red, Not Quite Navy, Bordering Blue, Going Gray, Creamy Caramel, and Garden Green Classic pads; watercolor brush; Natural hemp; Stampin' Dimensionals; crochet thread; needle

113 B

Prehistoric Paintings and Season's Greetings sets; Ruby Red, Naturals Ivory, and Old Olive card stock; Basic Black Classic pad; VersaMark pad; Basic Black marker; air art tool; Stampin' Pastels; Black embossing powder; paper crimper; Black hemp; Gold Mini Deco Fasteners; Stampin' Dimensionals; bleach

113 C

Prehistoric Paintings and All-Year Cheer I sets; Ruby Red, Basic Black, and Naturals Ivory card stock; Basic Black Classic pad; Basic Black marker; air art tool; Creamy Caramel eyelets; Black hemp; air art tool; jute; large needle

114 A

Classic Convertibles and All-Year Cheer I sets; Creamy Caramel, Ruby Red, Confetti Cream, and Basic Black card stock; Ruby Red and Basic Black Circle AlphaAccents; Basic Black and Ruby Red Classic pads; watercolor brush; Jumbo and 1/16" Circle punches; Black hemp; Stampin' Dimensionals

114 B

Classic Convertibles and All-Year Cheer II sets;[a] Ruby Red, Not Quite Navy, and Confetti Cream card stock; Not Quite Navy Classic pad; Silver eyelets; washers

114 C

All Aboard and All-Year Cheer II sets; Not Quite Navy, Confetti Cream, Basic Black, and Ruby Red card stock; Basic Black, Ruby Red, Creamy Caramel, and Not Quite Navy Classic Pads; Rectangle punch; Black grosgrain ribbon; watercolor brush; Ruby Red square eyelet; crochet thread

115 A

Born to Ride and Classic Alphabet sets; Not Quite Navy, Creamy Caramel, Confetti Cream, Basic Black, and Ruby Red card stock; Not Quite Navy Classic pad; Black eyelets

115 B

Born to Ride set; Creamy Caramel, Confetti Cream, Basic Black, and Ruby Red card stock; Creamy Caramel and Ruby Red Classic pads; Real Red eyelets; Stampin' Dimensionals; Natural hemp

115 C

Tractor Time and All-Year Cheer II sets; Not Quite Navy, Garden Green, Ruby Red, Confetti Cream, and Creamy Caramel card stock; Not Quite Navy Classic pad; Creamy Caramel eyelets; Natural hemp; Stampin' Dimensionals; 1/8" Circle punch

115 D

Tractor Time and God Bless sets; Garden Green, Confetti Cream, Not Quite Navy, and Ruby Red card stock; Basic Black, Ruby Red, Creamy Caramel, Garden Green, and Not Quite Navy Classic pads; watercolor brush; needle; crochet thread

116 A

Letters from Friends set; Creamy Caramel, Ultrasmooth Vanilla, Radiant White vellum, and Chocolate Chip card stock; Brocade Blue, Basic Black, Chocolate Chip, Bordering Blue, and Creamy Caramel Classic pads; Gold Encore! pad; Gold Glory embossing powder; stipple brush; Neutrals fiber; crochet thread; button

116 B

Days Gone By and All-Year Cheer III sets; Hand-Stitched background stamp; Baroque Burgundy, Creamy Caramel, Bordering Blue, and Ultrasmooth Vanilla card stock; Baroque Burgundy tag sheets; Close to Cocoa, Baroque Burgundy, and Creamy Caramel Classic pads; stipple brush; watercolor brush; Ivory wide organdy ribbon; Stampin' Dimensionals; Silver Mini Deco Fasteners; Classy Copper embossing powder; needle

116 C

Letters from Friends set; Close to Cocoa, Creamy Caramel, and Ultrasmooth Vanilla card stock; Creamy Caramel stationery box; Chocolate Chip and Close to Cocoa Classic pads; stipple brush

116 D

Days Gone By and All-Year Cheer II sets; Confetti White, Creamy Caramel, and Baroque Burgundy card stock; Basic Black, Old Olive, Creamy Caramel, Baroque Burgundy, and More Mustard Classic pads; watercolor brush; Ivory wide organdy ribbon; button; thread

117 A

Parisian Plaza and All-Year Cheer II sets; By Definition background stamp; Ultrasmooth Vanilla, Bordering Blue, and Night of Navy card stock; Victorian Designer Series vellum; Night of Navy and Bordering Blue Classic pads; Brocade Blue square eyelet; Regal Tones fiber; stipple brush

117 B

Parisian Plaza and All-Year Cheer II sets; Baroque Burgundy, Ultrasmooth Vanilla, and Night of Navy pouch box & tag sheets; Baroque Burgundy tag sheet; Night of Navy Classic pad; Basic Black marker; Night of Navy eyelet; Navy wide organdy ribbon; bleach; crochet thread

117 C

Travels Abroad set; Creamy Caramel, Night of Navy, Brocade Blue, and Baroque Burgundy card stock; Night of Navy, Brocade Blue, Creamy Caramel, and Baroque Burgundy Classic pads; watercolor brushes; stipple brush

118 A

Dream Catcher, The Shape of Things, and Birthday Greetings sets; Really Rust, Night of Navy, and Kraft card stock; Basic Black, Ruby Red, Really Rust, and Night of Navy Classic pads; watercolor brush; 1/8" Circle punch; Natural hemp; bleach

118 B

Dream Catcher set; Really Rust, Night of Navy, and Confetti Tan card stock; Really Rust and Night of Navy Classic pads; 1/16" Circle punch; Natural hemp

118 C

Liberty for All set; Night of Navy, Confetti White, and Real Red card stock; Real Red and Confetti White tag sheets; Real Red and Night of Navy Classic pads; Night of Navy eyelet

119 A

Friendship's Journey set; Night of Navy, Really Rust, and Confetti White (dyed with Really Rust ink) mulberry paper; Orange and White (dyed with Really Rust ink) mulberry paper; Basic Black, Night of Navy, and Really Rust Classic pads; watercolor brush; 1/8" Circle punch; Gold metallic cord; Stampin' Dimensionals; beads

119 B

Friendship's Journey and Classic Alphabet sets; Filigree background stamp; Confetti Tan, Real Red, and Night of Navy card stock; Creamy Caramel, Night of Navy, and Real Red Classic pads; 1/16" Circle punch; Gold metallic cord; Ivory wide organdy ribbon

119 C

World Traveler set; Kraft, Real Red, and Night of Navy card stock; VersaMark pad; Night of Navy, Real Red, and Really Rust Classic pads; watercolor brush; Creamy Caramel eyelets; Natural hemp; notepad

120 A

Elegant Ornaments and All-Year Cheer I sets; Antique background stamp; Mellow Moss, Barely Banana, and Ultrasmooth White card stock; More Mustard and Old Olive Classic pads; Stampin' Dimensionals; Neutrals fiber

120 B

Toile Blossoms and Elegant Greetings sets; Barely Banana, Ultrasmooth Vanilla, and Old Olive card stock; Old Olive Classic pad; Scallop scissors; Olive Green wide organdy ribbon; Gold metallic cord; Barely Banana small flower eyelet

121 A

Many Thanks set; Antique background and Avian Toile stamps; Barely Banana, Old Olive, and Ultrasmooth Vanilla card stock; Olive mulberry paper; Old Olive Classic pad; watercolor brush; 1/16" Circle punch; Gold metallic cord; Stampin' Dimensional; bleach

121 B
Birthday Greetings set; Antique background and Pastoral Toile stamps; Ultrasmooth Vanilla, Old Olive, and Radiant White vellum card stock; Olive Green mulberry paper; Old Olive Classic pad; Top Boss pad; Gold Glory embossing powder; Vanilla oval eyelet; 1/8" and 1/16" Circle punches; Olive Green wide organdy ribbon; Gold metallic cord; Stampin' Dimensionals; Gold Mini Deco Fasteners; button

122 A
Sun, Moon & Stars and Mini Mates set; Not Quite Navy and Barely Banana card stock; Not Quite Navy Classic pad; VersaMark pad; VersaMarker; Gold Glory embossing powder; Stampin' Dimensionals; 26-gauge Wire Works

122 B
Sun, Moon & Stars set; Barely Banana, Bordering Blue, and Night of Navy card stock; VersaMark pad; Gold detail embossing powder; Stampin' Dimensionals; Gold Mini Deco Fasteners; 26-gauge Wire Works

122 C
Celtic Knots set; Confetti White, Not Quite Navy, and Rose Red card stock; Rose Red and Not Quite Navy Classic pads; VersaMark pad; watercolor brush; Crystal Clear pad; Stampin' Dimensionals; paper crimper; Gold Mini Deco Fasteners

123 A
Beautiful Batik and All-Year Cheer II sets; Not Quite Navy, Barely Banana, and Rose Red card stock; Not Quite Navy Classic pad; VersaMark pad; Stampin' Pastels; paper crimper; Baroque Burgundy eyelets; Cream grosgrain ribbon

123 B
Beautiful Batik and Alphabet Fun Upper sets; Batik wheel; Rose Red, Ultrasmooth Vanilla, and Not Quite Navy card stock; Rose Red and Not Quite Navy Craft pads; journaling marker; 1/16" Circle punch; Red hemp; needle; bleach

124 A
By Design and Love without End sets; Not Quite Navy, More Mustard, Cameo Coral, Old Olive, and Naturals White card stock; Old Olive, Cameo Coral, More Mustard, and Not Quite Navy Classic pads; Stampin' Dimensionals

124 B
The Shape of Things and Spring Garden sets; Old Olive, Naturals White, and Cameo Coral card stock; Old Olive and Cameo Coral Classic pads; Spring Moss grosgrain ribbon; Mellow Moss eyelet; Stampin' Dimensionals; crochet thread

125 A
Asian Art set; Bamboo II background stamp; More Mustard, Not Quite Navy, and Old Olive card stock; Basic Black Craft pad; Gold Encore! pad; paper crimper; stamping sponge; Gold Glory embossing powder; 1/16" Circle punch; Gold metallic cord; Stampin' Dimensionals

125 B
Mini Mates and Little Shapes sets; More Mustard, Cameo Coral, and Naturals White card stock; Candy Designer Series vellum; Cameo Coral Circle AlphaAccents; Pretty in Pink and Positively Pink Classic pads; Pretty in Pink, More Mustard, and Barely Banana eyelets

125 C
Little Shapes and Classic Alphabet sets; By Definition background stamp; Not Quite Navy, Cameo Coral, and Naturals White card stock; Not Quite Navy and Cameo Coral Classic pads

126 A
Art of the Orient, Bamboo II, and Kanji sets; Bordering Blue, Rose Red, Ultrasmooth White, and Radiant White vellum card stock; Bordering Blue Classic pad; bamboo skewer; crochet thread; needle

126 B
Kanji and Little Shapes sets; Bamboo II background stamp; Sage Shadow, Rose Red, Radiant White vellum, and Ultrasmooth White card stock; Sage Shadow Classic pad; 26-gauge Wire Works; beads; needle

126 C
Oriental Paintings set; Bamboo II background stamp; Bordering Blue, Rose Red, Radiant White vellum, Sage Shadow, and Confetti White card stock; Basic Black, Bordering Blue, Rose Red, and Sage Shadow Classic pads; watercolor brush; Stampin' Dimensionals; 22-gauge Wire Works

127 A
Baroque Border set; Radiant White vellum, Bordering Blue, Confetti White, and Rose Red card stock; Confetti White tag sheet; Bordering Blue Craft pad; journaling marker; Bordering Blue eyelets; White narrow organdy ribbon; button; crochet thread; needle

128 A
Steppin' Style set; Barely Banana, Only Orange, Pretty in Pink, and Ultrasmooth White card stock; Basic Black, Only Orange, Positively Pink, Pretty in Pink, and Barely Banana Classic pads; watercolor brush; Pretty in Pink eyelets; Stampin' Dimensionals; embroidery floss

128 B
Recipe Fun set; Creamy Caramel and Ultrasmooth White card stock; Basic Black, Creamy Caramel, Ruby Red, Close to Cocoa, Chocolate Chip, and Mellow Moss Classic pads; Basic Black marker; watercolor brush

128 C
Steppin' Style set; Swirls & Blossoms background stamp; Pretty in Pink, Barely Banana, Rose Romance, Ultrasmooth White, and Radiant White vellum card stock; VersaMark pad; Rose Romance Classic pad; watercolor brush; Barely Banana eyelets; Rose grosgrain ribbon; crochet thread; buttons; needle

129 A
Love without End, Quirky Alphabet Upper, and Quirky Alphabet Lower sets; Positively Pink, Only Orange, and Ultrasmooth White card stock; Ultrasmooth White Circle AlphaAccents, Jrs.; Positively Pink, Green Galore, and Only Orange Circle AlphaAccents; Only Orange, Gable Green, and Positively Pink Craft pads; font CD; Stampin' Dimensionals; Love without End brass template

129 B
Love without End set; Positively Pink and Ultrasmooth White card stock; Positively Pink, Gable Green, and Only Orange Classic pads; white circle metal edge tag; Positively Pink eyelets; Love without End brass template; 22-gauge Wire Works

129 C
The Fine Print set; Barely Banana, Rose Romance, and Ultrasmooth White card stock; Candy Designer Series vellum; Rose Romance Classic pad; Barely Banana and Pretty in Pink eyelets; Scallop scissors

129 D
The Fine Print and All-Year Cheer I sets; Barely Banana, Only Orange, Positively Pink, Rose Romance, and Ultrasmooth White card stock; Candy Designer Series vellum; Only Orange and Positively Pink Classic pads; Positively Pink and Only Orange eyelets; 1/16" Circle punch; Rose grosgrain ribbon; embroidery floss

130 A
Wreath of Roses set; By Definition background stamp; Positively Pink, Lovely Lilac, and Confetti White card stock; Positively Pink, Basic Black, Green Galore, Barely Banana, and Lovely Lilac Classic pads; watercolor brushes; Stampin' Dimensionals; Purple hemp; 1/16" Circle punch

130 B
Wreath of Roses set; Filigree background stamp; Positively Pink, Lovely Lilac, Marvelous Magenta, Gable Green, Green Galore, and Radiant White vellum card stock; Basic Black Classic pad; VersaMark pad; 1/8" Circle punch; Rose grosgrain ribbon; Stampin' Dimensionals; crochet thread

130 C
You Are My Sunshine set; Lovely Lilac, Positively Pink, and Confetti White card stock; Basic Black, Summer Sun, Positively Pink, Lovely Lilac, and Green Galore Classic pads; watercolor brush; Stampin' Dimensionals; Natural hemp; 1/16" Circle punch; button

130 D
You Are My Sunshine set; Positively Pink, Confetti White, and Marvelous Magenta card stock; Positively Pink, Lovely Lilac, Marvelous Magenta, Basic Black, Summer Sun, and Garden Green Classic pads; watercolor brush; Orchid grosgrain ribbon; Positively Pink large flower eyelet; crochet thread; button

131 A
I Like Your Style set; Ultrasmooth Vanilla, Lavender lace, Marvelous Magenta, Lovely Lilac, and Green Galore card stock; Basic Black, Marvelous Magenta, Green Galore, and Lovely Lilac Classic pads; Green Galore, Lovely Lilac, and Baroque Burgundy eyelets; 26-gauge Wire Works; Stampin' Dimensionals; watercolor brush; bleach; sewing machine and thread

131 B
I Like Your Style set; Marvelous Magenta, Ultrasmooth Vanilla, Green Galore, and Lovely Lilac card stock; Basic Black, Green Galore, Garden Green, Lovely Lilac, Lavender Lace, Marvelous Magenta, and Orchid Opulence Classic pads; watercolor brush; paper crimper; buttons; string

131 C
Espress Yourself set; Green Galore, Positively Pink, and Confetti White card stock; Basic Black, Green Galore, Lovely Lilac, Garden Green, and Positively Pink Classic pads; watercolor brush; 1/16" Circle punch; Natural hemp; Positively Pink eyelet

131 D
Espress Yourself set; Positively Pink, Gable Green, and Confetti White card stock; Basic Black, Barely Banana, Positively Pink, Lovely Lilac, and Green Galore Classic pads; watercolor brush; 1/16" Circle punch; Natural hemp

132 A
Beary Best set; Stipple Plaid background stamp; Gable Green, Rose Romance, and Confetti White card stock; Basic Black, Gable Green, Close to Cocoa, Rose Romance, Lovely Lilac, and Summer Sun Classic pads; watercolor brush; crochet thread; button

132 B
Beary Best set; Teddy Time wheel; Brocade Blue, Confetti White, and Rose Romance card stock; Basic Black, Rose Romance, Brocade Blue, Lovely Lilac, Close to Cocoa, and Green Galore Classic pads; Brocade Blue cartridge; watercolor brush; paper crimper; Stampin' Dimensionals; Rose grosgrain ribbon

133 A
Pocket Fun and Classic Alphabet sets; Just Jeans background stamp; Gable Green, Brocade Blue, Night of Navy, and Confetti White card stock; Basic Black, Brocade Blue, Night of Navy, Gable Green, Green Galore, and Rose Romance Classic pads; journaling marker; watercolor brush; Silver eyelets; 1/2" Circle punch

133 B
Basket of Kindness set; Gable Green, Confetti White, and Positively Pink card stock; Basic Black, Creamy Caramel, Positively Pink, Lovely Lilac, and Gable Green Classic pads; watercolor brush; Positively Pink eyelet; Rose grosgrain ribbon; Stampin' Dimensionals

134 A
Cute Critters and Fresh Fillers sets; Sage Shadow, Real Red, and Confetti White card stock; Swirls printed vellum; Basic Black, Bordering Blue, Going Gray, Positively Pink, Real Red, Sage Shadow, and Summer Sun Classic pads; Stampin' Dimensionals; 1/8" Circle punch; Mellow Moss and Real Red eyelets; Red grosgrain ribbon

134 B
Cute Critters, Fresh Fillers, and All-Year Cheer II sets; Confetti White, Real Red, Radiant White vellum, and Sage Shadow card stock; Basic Black, Chocolate Chip, Real Red, Going Gray, and Sage Shadow Classic pads; watercolor brush; Silver Mini Deco Fasteners; 26-gauge Wire Works; embroidery floss; needle

134 C
Hedgehog Happiness set; Hedgie Play wheel; Confetti White, Cameo Coral, Ballet Blue, and Sage Shadow card stock; Basic Black, Ballet Blue, Cameo Coral, Sage Shadow, and Creamy Caramel Classic pads; Sage Shadow cartridge; watercolor brush; Scallop scissors; Corner Rounder punch; Sage Shadow eyelets; Bluebird grosgrain ribbon; crochet thread; buttons

135 A
Tea Time and Little Letters sets; Radiant White vellum, Confetti White, Rose Romance, Ballet Blue, Sage Shadow, and Barely Banana card stock; Rose Romance, Basic Black, and Sage Shadow Craft pads; VersaMark pad; font CD; buttons; needle; crochet thread

135 B
Tea Time and All-Year Cheer I sets; Swirls & Blossoms background stamp; Sage Shadow, Rose Romance, and Confetti White card stock; Pretty in Pink, Sage Shadow, and Rose Romance Classic pads; 1/16" Circle punch; Stampin' Dimensionals; Pretty in Pink small flower eyelets; sewing machine and thread; crochet thread

136 A
Little Boys set; Stipple Plaid background stamp; Creamy Caramel, Baroque Burgundy, Not Quite Navy, and Confetti Cream card stock; Creamy Caramel, Basic Black, Not Quite Navy, Barely Banana, Close to Cocoa, Baroque Burgundy, Blush Blossom, Chocolate Chip, Bliss Blue, and Garden Green Classic pads; watercolor brush; 1/16" Circle punch; Natural hemp

136 B
Fairyland set; Not Quite Navy, Baroque Burgundy, Radiant White vellum, and Confetti Cream card stock; Basic Black, Baroque Burgundy, Barely Banana, Blush Blossom, Not Quite Navy, and Night of Navy Classic pads; VersaMark pad; Interference Violet Pearl Ex; watercolor brush; Burgundy wide organdy ribbon

136 C
Fairyland set; Confetti Cream and Baroque Burgundy card stock; Confetti White tag sheet; Burgundy mulberry paper; Basic Black, Barely Banana, Creamy Caramel, Taken with Teal, Baroque Burgundy, Blush Blossom, Gable Green, and Forest Foliage Classic pads; watercolor brush; Ivory narrow organdy ribbon; Stampin' Dimensionals; crochet thread

137 A
Flowers & Friends and All-Year Cheer II sets; Mellow Moss, Barely Banana, Baroque Burgundy, and Ultrasmooth Vanilla card stock; Brocade Blue, Baroque Burgundy, and Mellow Moss Classic pads; Stampin' Dimensionals; button; string

137 B
Flowers & Friends and All-Year Cheer I sets; Kraft, Not Quite Navy, Ultrasmooth Vanilla, and Confetti White card stock; Confetti White and Baroque Burgundy tag sheets; Baroque Burgundy and Not Quite Navy Classic pads; Stampin' Dimensionals; Night of Navy eyelets; raffia; Natural hemp; button; string

137 C
You Warm My Heart set; Hand-Stitched background stamp; Not Quite Navy, Baroque Burgundy, and Confetti Cream card stock; Not Quite Navy, Basic Black, Garden Green, Barely Banana, and Baroque Burgundy Classic pads; VersaMark pad; watercolor brush; 1/16" Circle punch; Black embossing powder; crochet thread

138 A
Pretty Peacocks and Many Thanks sets; Pretty Paisley background stamp; Taken with Teal, Green Galore, and Naturals Ivory card stock; Basic Black, Tempting Turquoise, Taken with Teal, Green Galore, Creamy Caramel, and Basic Black Classic pads; watercolor brush; Green Galore eyelet; Green hemp; Stampin' Dimensionals

138 B
Pretty Peacocks and Simple Sayings II sets; Not Quite Navy, Taken with Teal, and Confetti Cream card stock; Basic Black, Taken with Teal, Green Galore, Not Quite Navy, Creamy Caramel, and Tempting Turquoise Classic pads; VersaMark pad; watercolor brush; Spring Green and True Blue Pearl Ex

138 C
Cold-Weather Friends and All-Year Cheer I; Basic Black, Not Quite Navy, Almost Amethyst, and Going Gray Classic pads; watercolor brush; Stampin' Dimensionals; 1/8" Circle punch; Natural hemp

138 D
Cold-Weather Friends and Fun Phrases sets; Not Quite Navy, Ultrasmooth Vanilla, Perfect Plum, and Almost Amethyst card stock; Basic Black, Not Quite Navy, and Perfect Plum Classic pads; watercolor brushes; Natural hemp; Perfect Plum eyelets

139 A
Equestrian Dream and Birthday Greetings sets; Not Quite Navy, Creamy Caramel, and Close to Cocoa card stock; Chocolate Chip and Going Gray Classic pads; VersaMark pad; Black detail embossing powder; watercolor brush; Black eyelets; twig; bleach

139 B
Bird Watcher and Classic Alphabet sets; Antique Cracking background stamp; Creamy Caramel, Not Quite Navy, Close to Cocoa, and Ultrasmooth Vanilla card stock; Basic Black, Ruby Red, Summer Sun, Close to Cocoa, Green Galore, Chocolate Chip, Not Quite Navy, and Forest Foliage Classic pads; watercolor brush; Natural hemp; 1/8" Circle punch; notepad; twig

139 C
Bird Watcher set; Harlequin background stamp; Brocade Blue, Naturals Ivory, Creamy Caramel, and Not Quite Navy card stock; Basic Black, Not Quite Navy, Creamy Caramel, and Brocade Blue Classic pads; White Craft pad; watercolor brush; Stampin' Dimensionals; excelsior; twig

140 A
In the Wild set; Creamy Caramel, Basic Black, and Chocolate Chip card stock; Basic Black and Chocolate Chip Classic pads; watercolor brush; paper crimper; Creamy Caramel eyelets; Black hemp; Stampin' Dimensionals; bleach

140 B
In the Wild and All-Year Cheer I sets; By Definition background stamp; Old Olive, Confetti Cream, Really Rust, Creamy Caramel, Mellow Moss, and Basic Black card stock; Mellow Moss and Old Olive Classic pads; Gold Mini Deco Fasteners

140 C
In the Outback set; Antique Cracking background stamp; Really Rust, Old Olive, Basic Black, and Ultrasmooth Vanilla card stock; Ultrasmooth Vanilla and Basic Black tag sheets; Basic Black and Really Rust Classic pads; font CD; Old Olive eyelets; Natural hemp

141 A
On the Farm and Simple Sayings sets; Chocolate Chip, Basic Black, Really Rust, Creamy Caramel, Mellow Moss, and Confetti Cream card stock; Basic Black, Chocolate Chip, Blush Blossom, Pretty in Pink, Going Gray, Ruby Red, Really Rust, Old Olive, and Mellow Moss Classic pads; watercolor brush; crochet thread; needle

141 B
On the Farm and Simple Sayings II sets; Ruby Red, Brocade Blue, and Confetti Cream card stock; Basic Black, Ruby Red, Brocade Blue, Going Gray, Creamy Caramel, Blush Blossom, Garden Green, and Old Olive Classic pads; watercolor brush; Creamy Caramel eyelets; Natural hemp

141 C
Brushstroke Horses, Classic Alphabet, and Simple Sayings sets; Wild Horses wheel; Really Rust, Basic Black, Creamy Caramel, and Confetti Cream card stock; Basic Black, Really Rust, and Creamy Caramel Classic pads; Really Rust cartridge; watercolor brush; 1/16" Circle punch; Black hemp

142 A
Pines and Classic Alphabet sets; Mellow Moss and Confetti Tan card stock; large kraft gift box; Mellow Moss, Creamy Caramel, and Chocolate Chip Classic pads; Mellow Moss and Chocolate Chip Craft pads; Crystal Clear embossing powder; Natural hemp; Mellow Moss eyelet

142 B
Pines and Birthday Greetings sets; Chocolate Chip, Close to Cocoa, Mellow Moss, and Naturals Ivory card stock; Mellow Moss and Chocolate Chip Classic pads; paper crimper; stamping sponge; 1/16" and 1/8" Circle punches; Natural hemp; Stampin' Dimensionals

142 C
Good Times set; Great Outdoors wheel; Groovy Lines background stamp; Mellow Moss, Confetti Cream, Basic Black, and Confetti Tan card stock; Basic Black and Mellow Moss Classic pads; Basic Black cartridge; VersaMark pad; Crystal Clear embossing powder; 26-gauge Wire Works

143 A
Yukon and Itty Bitty Backgrounds sets; Stipple Plaid background stamp; Mellow Moss, Chocolate Chip, Creamy Caramel, and Confetti Cream card stock; Basic Black, Chocolate Chip, Creamy Caramel, Going Gray, Bordering Blue, Mellow Moss, Forest Foliage, Close to Cocoa, Garden Green, Brocade Blue, and Eggplant Envy Classic pads; watercolor brush; Stampin' Dimensionals; Taupe grosgrain ribbon

143 B
Yukon and Simple Sayings II sets; Chocolate Chip, Mellow Moss, Creamy Caramel, and Ultrasmooth Vanilla card stock; Creamy Caramel, Bliss Blue, Brocade Blue, Garden Green, Basic Black, and Chocolate Chip Classic pads; watercolor brush; 1/16" Circle punch; rubber brayer; Natural hemp; Stampin' Dimensionals

143 C
Wolf, The Shape of Things, and All-Year Cheer II sets; Close to Cocoa, Chocolate Chip, Mellow Moss, and Naturals Ivory card stock; Basic Black, Chocolate Chip, Close to Cocoa, Really Rust, Mellow Moss, and Garden Green Classic pads; watercolor brush; vellum circle metal edge tag; Silver Mini Deco Fastener; paper crimper; Natural hemp; bleach

144 A
Canine Capers and Simple Sayings II sets; Close to Cocoa, Creamy Caramel, Barely Banana, and Confetti White card stock; Basic Black, Going Gray, Chocolate Chip, Close to Cocoa, More Mustard, Creamy Caramel, Really Rust, Barely Banana, and Cameo Coral Classic pads; watercolor brush; paper crimper; Cream grosgrain ribbon; Gold Mini Deco Fasteners

144 B
Purrfect set; Barely Banana, Brocade Blue, Confetti White, and Creamy Caramel card stock; Basic Black, Barely Banana, Creamy Caramel, Brocade Blue, and Cameo Coral Classic pads; watercolor brush; Southwest Corner punch; Stampin' Dimensionals; 1/16" Circle punch; crochet thread

145 A
Fishy Friends and Simple Sayings sets; Creamy Caramel, Cameo Coral, Barely Banana, and Confetti White card stock; VersaMark pad; Basic Black, Creamy Caramel, Cameo Coral, and Barely Banana Classic pads; watercolor brush; paper crimper; 1/16" Circle punch; Natural hemp; Stampin' Dimensionals

145 B
Fishy Friends, The Shape of Things, Little Shapes, and Simple Sayings II sets; Confetti White, Barely Banana, and Brocade Blue card stock; Brocade Blue, Bordering Blue, Basic Black, and Cameo Coral Classic pads; watercolor brush

145 C
Flutterbys and All-Year Cheer II sets; Butterfly wheel; Cameo Coral, Barely Banana, Confetti White, and Brocade Blue card stock; VersaMark pad; Cameo Coral, Barely Banana, and Brocade Blue Classic pads; Brocade Blue Craft pad; White cartridge; stamping sponge; Stampin' Dimensionals; French Blue grosgrain ribbon; White eyelets

146 A
All-Year Cheer II set; Stipple Butterfly stamp; Ballet Blue, Mellow Moss, Barely Banana, and Confetti White card stock; Celery mulberry paper; Basic Black, Barely Banana, Creamy Caramel, Ballet Blue, and Mellow Moss Classic pads; watercolor brush; Stampin' Dimensionals

146 B
In the Sky set; Brilliant Blue, Barely Banana, Confetti White, Ballet Blue, and Brilliant Blue card stock; Brilliant Blue, Barely Banana, and Ballet Blue Classic pads; watercolor brush; buttons; crochet thread

146 C
In the Sky and Classic Alphabet sets; Barely Banana, Brilliant Blue, Confetti White, and Chocolate Chip card stock; Chocolate Chip and Barely Banana Classic pads; watercolor brush; Barely Banana eyelets; Natural hemp; Stampin' Dimensionals; bleach; crochet thread; needle

146 D
Bunch o' Bugs, Itty Bitty Backgrounds, and All-Year Cheer II sets; Dragonfly wheel; Barely Banana, Mellow Moss, Real Red, Brilliant Blue, and Confetti White card stock; Real Red, Mellow Moss, and Brilliant Blue Classic pads; Barely Banana cartridge; Brilliant Blue eyelets; Natural hemp; Jumbo Circle punch

147 A
Wide Open Spaces and Versatile Verses sets; Mellow Moss, Close to Cocoa, Barely Banana, and Confetti White card stock; Mellow Moss, Barely Banana, and Creamy Caramel Classic pads; stipple brush; Mellow Moss eyelets; natural hemp; Stampin' Dimensionals

147 B
Bunch o' Bugs and Classic Alphabet sets; Bitty Bugs wheel; Mellow Moss, Ballet Blue, and Confetti White card stock; Ballet Blue and Mellow Moss Classic pads; Mellow Moss cartridge; Stampin' Dimensionals; French Blue grosgrain ribbon

148 A
Cute as a Bug set; Confetti White, Old Olive, and Real Red card stock; Basic Black, Not Quite Navy, Old Olive, and Real Red Classic pads; watercolor brush; Real Red eyelets; 26-gauge Wire Works; 1/16" Circle punch

148 B
Cute as a Bug set; Real Red and Basic Black card stock; Real Red and Ultrasmooth White tag sheets; Basic Black Classic pad; Basic Black and Real Red markers; watercolor pencils; 1/2" Circle punch; stamping sponge; Black eyelets; Red grosgrain ribbon; crochet thread

148 C
Wonderful Wings and Classic Alphabet sets; French Script background stamp; Not Quite Navy, Old Olive, Radiant White vellum, and Ultrasmooth Vanilla card stock; Old Olive and Basic Black Classic pads; VersaMark pad; Stampin' Pastels; Gold Mini Deco Fasteners; Stampin' Dimensionals; stamping sponges

149 A
Inspirationals and Fun Phrases sets; Hand-Stitched background stamp; Old Olive, Confetti White, and Real Red card stock; Basic Black, Yoyo Yellow, Not Quite Navy, Real Red, and Old Olive Classic pads; VersaMark pad; watercolor brush; Crystal Clear embossing powder; Natural hemp; needle

149 B

All God's Children set; Stipple Plaid background stamp; Not Quite Navy, Real Red, and Confetti White card stock; Basic Black, Real Red, Summer Sun, Blush Blossom, Only Orange, Old Olive, and Brocade Blue Classic pads; watercolor brush; 1/16" Circle punch; vellum square metal edge tag; Scallop scissors; crochet thread; button

149 C

All God's Children and Fun Phrases sets; Hand-Stitched background stamp; Real Red, Confetti White, Not Quite Navy, and Old Olive card stock; Old Olive tag sheet; Basic Black, Not Quite Navy, Real Red, and Old Olive Classic pads; watercolor brush; Gold eyelet; Stampin' Dimensionals; 1/16" Circle stamp; Natural hemp

150 A

Two by Two set; Creamy Caramel, Brocade Blue, Ruby Red, and Confetti White card stock; Basic Black, Eggplant Envy, Going Gray, Pretty in Pink, Creamy Caramel, Really Rust, Ruby Red, Barely Banana, Taken with Teal, Brocade Blue, Close to Cocoa, Chocolate Chip, Only Orange, and More Mustard Classic pads; watercolor brush; 1/16" Circle punch; Natural hemp

150 B

Say It with Scriptures and All God's Children sets; Stipple Plaid background stamp; Really Rust, Confetti White, Brocade Blue, and Creamy Caramel card stock; Basic Black, Really Rust, Blush Blossom, Close to Cocoa, Creamy Caramel, Brocade Blue, Bordering Blue, and Ruby Red Classic pads; watercolor brush; White grosgrain ribbon; crochet thread; needle

151 A

Hope set; Filigree background stamp; Creamy Caramel, Confetti White, and Ruby Red card stock; Creamy Caramel and Ruby Red Classic pads; crochet thread; button

151 B

God Bless and Elegant Ornaments sets; Ruby Red, Chocolate Chip, Creamy Caramel, and Confetti Cream card stock; Basic Black and Creamy Caramel Classic pads; Ruby Red Craft pad; Crystal Clear embossing powder; stipple brush; Stampin' Dimensionals; Neutrals fiber

152 A

Little Inspirations and Beyond the Basics sets; Bliss Blue, Brocade Blue, Positively Pink, and Naturals White card stock; Basic Black, Bliss Blue, Positively Pink, and Old Olive Classic pads; watercolor brush; White eyelets; Regal Tones fiber

153 A

Fun Phrases, By Design, and Baby Firsts sets; Bliss Blue, Barely Banana, and Ballet Blue card stock; Bliss Blue and Ballet Blue Classic pads

153 B

Simple Sayings II, You Are My Sunshine, and By Design sets; Lavender Lace, Ultrasmooth Vanilla, Brocade Blue, Cameo Coral, and Barely Banana card stock; Basic Black, Cameo Coral, Barely Banana, Mellow Moss, Lavender Lace, Brocade Blue, Bliss Blue, and Blush Blossom Classic pads; watercolor brush

154 A

Elegant Greetings and Baroque Border sets; Tempting Turquoise, Radiant White vellum, and Ultrasmooth White card stock; Basic Black Classic pad; VersaMark pad; vellum square metal edge tag; Stampin' Dimensionals; White wide organdy ribbon

154 B

Simple Sayings and Love without End sets; Positively Pink, Yoyo Yellow, Tempting Turquoise, and Ultrasmooth White card stock; Tempting Turquoise, Yoyo Yellow, Positively Pink, and Basic Black Classic pads; White eyelets

154 C

Vogue Verses and Simply Sweet sets; Tempting Turquoise, Ultrasmooth White, Positively Pink, and Green Galore card stock; Basic Black, Gable Green, Yoyo Yellow, Positively Pink, and Tempting Turquoise Classic pads; watercolor brush; Crystal Effects

155 A

Cheery Chat set; By Definition background stamp; Ultrasmooth White, Positively Pink, and Tempting Turquoise card stock; Tempting Turquoise Classic pad; Positively Pink, Green Galore, Only Orange, Yoyo Yellow, and Tempting Turquoise markers; Silver Mini Deco Fastener; Stampin' Dimensionals

156 A

Birthday Greetings and Sweet Treats sets; Confetti White, Positively Pink, and Only Orange card stock; Basic Black, Only Orange, Summer Sun, Ballet Blue, Positively Pink, and Green Galore Classic pads; watercolor brush; Green Galore, Positively Pink, Only Orange, and Yoyo Yellow eyelets

157 A

Many Thanks and Happy Hearts sets; Positively Pink, Ballet Blue, Gable Green, Ultrasmooth White, Pink Passion, and Only Orange card stock; Ultrasmooth White tag sheet; Gable Green, Only Orange, Ballet Blue, and Pink Passion Classic pads; Stampin' Dimensionals; 1/16" Circle punch; Only Orange eyelet; Tangerine grosgrain ribbon; 22-gauge Wire Works

157 B

All-Year Cheer I and Mini Mates sets; Brocade Blue, Ultrasmooth Vanilla, Only Orange, and Confetti Tan card stock; Swirls printed vellum; Only Orange, Positively Pink, Brilliant Blue, and Lovely Lilac Classic pads; Only Orange, Green Galore, Positively Pink, and Lovely Lilac markers; watercolor brush; stamping sponge; Bordering Blue, Only Orange, and Positively Pink eyelets; Natural hemp; Stampin' Dimensionals

158 A

Saludos and On the Line sets; Ultrasmooth White card stock; Splash Designer Series vellum; Brocade Blue, Bliss Blue, and Sage Shadow Classic pads; Brocade Blue square eyelets; Natural hemp; Stampin' Dimensionals; mini clothes pin

158 B

All-Year Cheer II and Hearts & Clovers sets; Brocade Blue, Rose Red, Barely Banana, and Ultrasmooth White card stock; Basic Black, Sage Shadow, Rose Red, Brocade Blue, and Barely Banana Classic pads; watercolor brush; Stampin' Dimensionals; crochet thread; needle; button

159 A

Happy Hearts and All-Year Cheer III sets; Rose Romance, Barely Banana, Rose Red, and Ultrasmooth White card stock; Rose Romance and Rose Red Classic pads; Stampin' Dimensionals; button; crochet thread

159 B

Hope for Comfort and Perfect Petals sets; Brocade Blue, Ultrasmooth White, and Barely Banana card stock; Basic Black, Barely Banana, Sage Shadow, Mellow Moss, Mauve Mist, Brocade Blue, and Orchid Opulence pads; watercolor brush; Subtles fiber

160 A

Itty Bitty Borders and All-Year Cheer I sets; Basic Black, Real Red, and Ultrasmooth White card stock; Basic Black Circle AlphaAccent; Ultrasmooth White tag sheet; Basic Black Classic pad; Real Red marker; air art tool; Real Red and Basic Black eyelets; Stampin' Dimensionals; string

160 B

Best Borders and All-Year Cheer I sets; Forest Foliage, Real Red, and Ultrasmooth White card stock; Basic Black, Real Red, and Forest Foliage Classic pads; blender pen; Forest Foliage eyelets

160 C

Best Borders and All-Year Cheer I sets; Checkerboard background stamp; Ultrasmooth White, Real Red, and Basic Black card stock; Basic Black, Real Red, Going Gray, and Forest Foliage Classic pads; watercolor brush; Black eyelets; 1/4" Circle punch; Corner Rounder punch; Red grosgrain ribbon

161 A

Petite Patterns and Good Times sets; Ultrasmooth White and Real Red card stock; Real Red and Basic Black Classic pads; vellum circle metal edge tag; Folk Heart punch; Natural hemp; Stampin' Dimensional; Real Red heart eyelets

161 B

Beyond the Basics, Borders Mini, and Good Times sets; Real Red and Ultrasmooth White card stock; Real Red and Basic Black Classic pads; watercolor brush; Stampin' Dimensional; Crystal Effects

161 C

Beyond the Basics, Borders Mini, and Mini Mates sets; Forest Foliage, Real Red, and Ultrasmooth White card stock; Forest Foliage, Real Red, and Basic Black Classic pads; Real Red and Forest Foliage markers; Real Red eyelets; Natural hemp

162 A

Background Basics and Good Times set; Blush Blossom, Mellow Moss, and Ultrasmooth White card stock; Mellow Moss tag sheet; Basic Black, Blush Blossom, and Mellow Moss Classic pads; watercolor brush; 1/16" and 1/8" Circle punches; Peach narrow organdy ribbon; Stampin' Dimensional; crochet thread

162 B

Border Builders and Simple Sayings II sets; Ultrasmooth White, Mellow Moss, Almost Amethyst, Barely Banana, and Blush Blossom card stock; Mellow Moss, Cameo Coral, Almost Amethyst, Blush Blossom, and Barely Banana Classic pads; watercolor brush; Stampin' Dimensionals; Natural hemp; Blush Blossom eyelets; needle

163 A

Perfect Plaids, Vegetable Garden, and Classic Alphabet sets; Barely Banana, Mellow Moss, and Ultrasmooth White card stock; Mellow Moss, Barely Banana, and Old Olive Classic pads; vellum circle metal edge tag; Stampin' Dimensionals; Barely Banana eyelet; 1/16" Circle punch; crochet thread

163 B

Mini Medleys and Classic Alphabet sets; Blush Blossom, Almost Amethyst, Barely Banana, Mellow Moss, and Ultrasmooth White card stock; Ultrasmooth White, Mellow Moss, and Barely Banana tag sheets; VersaMark pad; Almost Amethyst, Barely Banana, Blush Blossom, and Mellow Moss Craft pads; Silver Mini Deco Fasteners; Stampin' Dimensionals; Squares & Minis brass template; 1/2" and 1/8" Circle punches; pencil

164 A

Elegant Greetings set; Antique background stamp; Basic Black and Naturals White card stock; Basic Black Classic pad; VersaMark pad; Black embossing powder; White narrow organdy ribbon

165 A

Yeehaw and All-Year Cheer III sets; Pretty Paisley background stamp; Real Red and Basic Black card stock; Real Red tag sheet; Basic Black Classic pad; VersaMark pad; Sterling Silver embossing powder; Silver Mini Deco Fasteners

166 A

Classic Alphabet set; By Definition background stamp; Ruby Red and Kraft card stock; Basic Black Classic pad; Creamy Caramel eyelets; vellum square metal edge tag; Earth Tones fiber

167 A

All-Around Alphabet set; Highways & Byways background stamp; Ultrasmooth White, Kraft, Basic Black, and Ruby Red card stock; Ruby Red and Basic Black Classic pads; Basic Black marker; Black eyelet; crochet thread; needle

168 A

Etruscan and All-Year Cheer III sets; Vineyard background stamp; More Mustard and Really Rust card stock; Ultrasmooth Vanilla tag sheet; Really Rust and More Mustard Classic pads; More Mustard eyelet; Stampin' Dimensionals; Natural hemp; Ivory narrow organdy ribbon

169 A

Yeehaw and All-Year Cheer III sets; Just Jeans background stamp; Confetti White, Really Rust, More Mustard, and Creamy Caramel card stock; Basic Black, Really Rust, Creamy Caramel, Close to Cocoa, and More Mustard Classic pads; watercolor brush; Stampin' Dimensionals; Gold Mini Deco Fasteners; sewing machine and metallic thread

170 A

AlphaBuilders set; Just Jeans background stamp; Barely Banana, Real Red, Brocade Blue, and Ultrasmooth White card stock; Brocade Blue and Real Red Craft pads; Brocade Blue marker; font CD; buttons; crochet thread

170 B

AlphaBuilders, AlphaBuilders Accessories, and Background Basics sets; Barely Banana, Brocade Blue, Ultrasmooth White, and Real Red card stock; Real Red and Brocade Blue Classic pads; Stampin' Dimensionals; Real Red star eyelet; Regal Tones fiber

171 A

Crazy Alphabet and By Design sets; Barely Banana, Real Red, Brocade Blue, Radiant White vellum, and Ultrasmooth White card stock; Real Red and Brocade Blue Craft pads; Brocade Blue and Ruby Red square eyelets; font CD; Stampin' Dimensionals; crochet thread; needle

171 B

Crazy Alphabet and Crazy Alphabet Numbers sets; Groovy Lines background stamp; Real Red, Ultrasmooth White, and Brocade Blue card stock; Real Red and Brocade Blue Classic pads; Brocade Blue square eyelets

172 A

Crayon Fun Alphabet Upper and Crayon Cuties sets; Taken with Teal, Ultrasmooth Vanilla, and Barely Banana card stock; Taken with Teal and Pink Passion Craft pads; font CD

173 A

Alphabet Attitude Upper, Alphabet Attitude Lower, and Wide Open Spaces sets; Not Quite Navy, Barely Banana, Really Rust, and Ultrasmooth Vanilla card stock; Not Quite Navy Craft pad; VersaMark pad; font CD

173 B
Alphabet Appeal Upper, I Like Your Style, and Alphabet Appeal Lower sets; Not Quite Navy, Ultrasmooth Vanilla, Barely Banana, and Really Rust card stock; Basic Black, Going Gray, Not Quite Navy, Barely Banana, and Really Rust Classic pads; watercolor brush

174 A
AlphaBlocks set; By Definition background stamp; Mellow Moss, Brocade Blue, Pale Plum, Perfect Plum, and Ultrasmooth Vanilla card stock; Mellow Moss, Brocade Blue, and Perfect Plum Craft pads; journaling marker; Bordering Blue eyelets; Love without End brass template; paper crimper

174 B
All-Around Alphabet, By Design, and New Beginnings sets; Ultrasmooth Vanilla, Mellow Moss, and Brocade Blue card stock; Basic Black, Mellow Moss, and Brocade Blue Classic pads; Mellow Moss eyelets; Stampin' Dimensionals; 26-gauge Wire Works; 1/2" Circle punch; stamping sponge; watercolor brush

175 A
Classic Alphabet and Soft & Sweet sets; Perfect Plum, Pale Plum, Radiant White vellum, and Ultrasmooth Vanilla card stock; Perfect Plum and Pale Plum Craft pads; journaling marker; 1/4" and 1/2" Circle punches; Perfect Plum eyelets; Ivory narrow organdy ribbon

175 B
Bold Alphabet set; Groovy Lines background stamp; Perfect Plum, Pale Plum, Mellow Moss, and Brocade Blue card stock; Mellow Moss Square AlphaAccents; Ultrasmooth Vanilla Circle AlphaAccents, Jrs.; Brocade Blue Craft pad; journaling marker; crochet thread; needle

176 A
All Occasions and By Design sets; Brocade Blue, Night of Navy, and Ultrasmooth Vanilla card stock; Brocade Blue, Blush Blossom, and Barely Banana Classic pads; watercolor brush

176 B
Happy Birthday wheel; Brocade Blue, Naturals White, and Ruby Red card stock; Ruby Red and Bordering Blue Circle AlphaAccents; Brocade Blue cartridge; Stampin' Dimensionals; font CD; 26-gauge Wire Works

176 C
Bold Greetings Mini set; Swirls & Blossoms background stamp; Ruby Red, Naturals White, and Brocade Blue card stock; Ruby Red and Brocade Blue Classic pads; Brocade Blue square eyelets; French Blue grosgrain ribbon

177 A
Birthday Celebration set; Happy Birthday Greetings background stamp; Brocade Blue, Mellow Moss, and Naturals White card stock; Brocade Blue, Ballet Blue, Mellow Moss, and Barely Banana Classic pads; paper crimper; Stampin' Dimensionals; Subtles fiber

177 B
Birthday Celebration set; Mellow Moss, Naturals White, and Garden Green card stock; Mellow Moss Classic pad; VersaMark pad; 26-gauge Wire Works; Stampin' Dimensionals; White grosgrain ribbon

177 C
Let's Party set; Groovy Lines background stamp; Ultrasmooth Vanilla, Mellow Moss, Ruby Red, and Brocade Blue card stock; Mellow Moss, Brocade Blue, and Ruby Red Classic pads; Dazzling Diamonds glitter

178 A
Perfect Party and Simple Sayings II sets; Positively Pink, Green Galore, and Ultrasmooth White card stock; Positively Pink, Lovely Lilac, Only Orange, Basic Black, and Green Galore Classic pads; White Craft pad; paper crimper; Green Galore triangle eyelets; 1/16" Circle punch; Stampin' Dimensionals

178 B
Birthday Balloons and Classic Alphabet sets; Confetti Streamers wheel; Only Orange, Lovely Lilac, Ultrasmooth White, and Green Galore card stock; Positively Pink, Lovely Lilac, Only Orange, and Green Galore Classic pads; Only Orange and Green Galore cartridges; paper crimper; Scallop scissors; Stampin' Dimensionals; 26-gauge Wire Works

179 A
Sketch a Party and All-Year Cheer I sets; Lovely Lilac, Ultrasmooth White, Positively Pink, Only Orange, and Green Galore card stock; Ultrasmooth White tag sheet; Lovely Lilac and Positively Pink Classic pads; Green Galore, Only Orange, and Positively Pink markers; 1/8" Circle punch; paper crimper; embroidery floss

179 B
Just My Type and Alphablocks sets; Green Galore, Positively Pink, Lovely Lilac, Only Orange, and Ultrasmooth White card stock; Green Galore, Positively Pink, Lovely Lilac, and Only Orange Classic pads; Basic Black marker; Positively Pink, Only Orange, Green Galore, and Lovely Lilac eyelets

179 C
Just My Type set; Swirls & Blossoms background stamp; Green Galore and Ultrasmooth White card stock; Green Galore, Old Olive, and Positively Pink Classic pads; Basic Black marker; Stampin' Dimensionals; Olive Green wide organdy ribbon; Old Olive eyelet; crochet thread

180 A
Sweet Treats and Simple Sayings sets; Pretty in Pink, Confetti White, Rose Romance, Radiant White vellum, and Creamy Caramel card stock; Rose Romance, Pretty in Pink, Creamy Caramel, and Sage Shadow Classic pads; watercolor brush

180 B
Sweet Treats and Simple Sayings sets; Barely Banana, Rose Romance, Pretty in Pink, and Confetti White card stock; Basic Black, Creamy Caramel, Barely Banana, Rose Romance, Pretty in Pink, and Garden Green Classic pads; watercolor brush; 1/16" Circle punch; Silver Mini Deco Fasteners; Natural hemp; Stampin' Dimensionals

180 C
All-Year Cheer I set; Whimsical Flowers wheel; Creamy Caramel and Barely Banana card stock; VersaMark pad; Creamy Caramel cartridge; Natural hemp; button; crochet thread

180 D
Dot Invitation and Love without End sets; Rose Romance, Radiant White vellum, Pretty in Pink, and Confetti White card stock; Rose Romance and Rose Red Classic pads; Rose Red marker; White large circle eyelet; Rose grosgrain ribbon; crochet thread; needle

181 A
All-Year Cheer I and Simply Sweet sets; Happy Birthday Greetings background stamp; Positively Pink, Barely Banana, and Ultrasmooth White card stock; Positively Pink and Rose Red Classic pads; 1/16" Circle punch; Red hemp; Barely Banana small flower eyelet

181 B
Happy Birthday Greetings background stamp; Rose Romance, Pretty in Pink, Ultrasmooth White, and Radiant White vellum card stock; Rose Romance Classic pad; Folk Heart punch; crochet thread; needle; button

181 C
Wedding Elegance and Classic Alphabet sets; Rose Romance and Ultrasmooth White card stock; Candy Designer Series vellum; VersaMark pad; Rose Romance and Pretty in Pink Craft pads; Silver detail embossing powder; watercolor brush; Stampin' Dimensionals; Silver metallic cord; needle

182 A
A Lifetime of Love set; Bliss Blue, Kraft, and Cameo Coral card stock; VersaMark pad; Bliss Blue, Barely Banana, and Cameo Coral markers; Black embossing powder; White narrow organdy ribbon; bleach

182 B
Soft & Sweet set; Bliss Blue, Barely Banana, Ballet Blue, and Ultrasmooth White card stock; Splash Designer Series paper; Basic Black, Close to Cocoa, Barely Banana, Bliss Blue, Ballet Blue, and Brocade Blue Classic pads; watercolor brush; Scallop scissors; Bliss Blue eyelets; Stampin' Dimensionals; Bluebird grosgrain ribbon

182 C
Soft & Sweet set; Cameo Coral, Radiant White vellum, and Shimmery White card stock; Cameo Coral Classic pad; Positively Pink eyelets; Stampin' Dimensionals; string

183 A
New Beginnings set; Harlequin background stamp; Ultrasmooth White, Bliss Blue, Sage Shadow; and Brocade Blue card stock; Basic Black, Sage Shadow, Bliss Blue, and Brocade Blue Classic pads; watercolor brush; paper crimper; Light Blue narrow organdy ribbon; Sage Shadow and Bliss Blue eyelets; Stampin' Dimensionals; Frames & Borders brass template

183 B
New Beginnings set; Positively Pink, Barely Banana, Radiant White vellum, and Ultrasmooth White card stock; Candy Designer Series paper; Basic Black Classic pad; Positively Pink and Barely Banana markers; Stampin' Dimensionals; Scallop scissors; Barely Banana and Positively Pink eyelets; Light Pink wide organdy ribbon; Envelope Template Assortment II; string

183 C
Sketch an Event and Simple Sayings sets; Kraft, Ultrasmooth Vanilla, Brocade Blue, Ballet Blue, Radiant White vellum, and Bordering Blue card stock; Close to Cocoa, Ballet Blue, and Bordering Blue Classic pads; watercolor brush; stamping sponge; Bordering Blue eyelets; Corner Rounder punch; string

184 A
Cuddles & Tickles and All-Year Cheer II sets; Barely Banana, Ballet Blue, Mellow Moss, Ultrasmooth White, and Cameo Coral card stock; Barely Banana, Ballet Blue, Old Olive, and Cameo Coral Classic pads; watercolor brush

184 B
Baby Firsts sets; Cameo Coral, Mellow Moss, and Confetti White card stock; Basic Black, Blush Blossom, Cameo Coral, Mellow Moss, Bliss Blue, Bordering Blue, and Barely Banana Classic pads; watercolor brush; Natural hemp; Mellow Moss eyelets; sewing machine and thread

184 C
Baby Firsts and Classic Alphabet sets; Baby Time wheel; Ballet Blue, Mellow Moss, Barely Banana, and Ultrasmooth White card stock; Splash Designer Series paper; Brocade Blue, Blush Blossom, Mellow Moss, and Positively Pink Craft pads; Brocade Blue cartridge; watercolor pencils; watercolor brush; white circle metal edge tag; 1/8" Circle punch; Silver Mini Deco Fasteners; crochet thread

185 A
On the Line, Quirky Alphabet Upper, and Quirky Alphabet Lower sets; Barely Banana, Confetti White, and Cameo Coral card stock; Candy Designer Series vellum; Cameo Coral Craft pad; journaling marker; 26-gauge Wire Works; Barely Banana and Blush Blossom eyelets; Ivory narrow organdy ribbon; 1/16" Circle punch; embroidery thread; needle

185 B
On the Line set; Stipple Plaid background stamp; Barely Banana, Ballet Blue, and Ultrasmooth White card stock; Summer Sun and Ballet Blue Classic pads; Barely Banana eyelets; Blue hemp; Stampin' Dimensionals

185 C
Announcements set; Checkerboard background stamp; Ultrasmooth White, Ballet Blue, and Cameo Coral card stock; Cameo Coral and Ballet Blue Classic pads; Blue narrow organdy ribbon; Stampin' Dimensionals

186 A
Rubber Ducky and All-Year Cheer II sets; Hand-Stitched background stamp; Not Quite Navy, Real Red, and Confetti White card stock; Not Quite Navy, Summer Sun, Only Orange, and Real Red Classic pads; 1/16" and 1/8" Circle punches; Stampin' Dimensionals; Real Red eyelets; Silver star eyelet; metal washers; crochet thread

187 A
Build a 'Bot and Simple Sayings sets; Ruby Red, Not Quite Navy, and Confetti White card stock; Not Quite Navy, Ruby Red, and Going Gray Classic pads; Ruby Red square eyelets; metal washers

187 B
Dino-Mite and Quirky Alphabet Lower sets; Old Olive, Not Quite Navy, Confetti White, and Real Red card stock; Old Olive, and Not Quite Navy Craft Pads; VersaMark pad; Stampin' Dimensionals; font CD

187 C
Dino-Mite and All-Year Cheer I sets; Not Quite Navy, Real Red, Confetti White, and Old Olive card stock; Old Olive, Real Red, and Not Quite Navy Classic pads; Stampin' Dimensionals; large needle

188 A
To the Finish and Fresh Fillers sets; Summer Sun, Real Red, Ultrasmooth White, and Brilliant Blue card stock; Basic Black Classic pad; watercolor pencils; Stampin' Dimensionals; Black eyelets; Black hemp

188 B
To the Finish set; Brilliant Blue, Ultrasmooth White, Real Red, and Summer Sun card stock; Basic Black Classic pad; Real Red marker; watercolor pencils; 1/16" Circle punch; Stampin' Dimensionals; air art tool; Yellow hemp; Real Red eyelets

188 C
Yeehaw set; Creamy Caramel and Confetti White card stock; Real Red, Basic Black, Close to Cocoa, and More Mustard Classic pads; watercolor brush; 1/16" Circle punch; Silver Mini Deco Fasteners; Natural and Black hemp

190 A
Crayon Cuties and Crayon Fun Alphabet Upper sets; Crayon Fun wheel; Real Red, Brilliant Blue, Glorious Green, and Ultrasmooth White card stock; Glorious Green, Brilliant Blue, and Real Red Craft pads; Brilliant Blue cartridge; journaling marker; Blue hemp; Stampin' Dimensionals

190 B
Going Somewhere and Alphabet Fun Upper sets; Brilliant Blue, Glorious Green, Real Red, and Ultrasmooth White card stock; Glorious Green, Brilliant Blue, and Real Red Classic pads; 1/16" Circle punch; Blue hemp

190 C
Going Somewhere and All-Year Cheer II sets; Zoom wheel; Ultrasmooth White, Real Red, and Brilliant Blue card stock; die-cut basket box; Brilliant Blue Classic pad; Real Red cartridge; Blue hemp; Real Red eyelets; Stampin' Dimensionals; button; crochet thread; needle

191 A
Crayon Fun and Crayon Fun Alphabet sets; Just Jeans background stamp; Glorious Green, Brilliant Blue, and Ultrasmooth White card stock; Glorious Green and Brilliant Blue Classic pads; 1/16" Circle punch; Stampin' Dimensionals; Blue hemp

192 A
Teacher Talk set; Ruby Red Classic pad

192 B
Teacher Talk set; Checkerboard background stamp; More Mustard, Ruby Red, and Confetti Cream card stock; Ruby Red and More Mustard Classic pads; 1/16" Circle punch; Natural hemp; More Mustard square eyelets

192 C
Teacher Time, Itty Bitty Backgrounds, and Beyond the Basics sets; More Mustard, Confetti Cream, Garden Green, Ruby Red, and Basic Black card stock; Basic Black, More Mustard, Going Gray, Ruby Red, and Garden Green Classic pads; watercolor brush; Stampin' Dimensionals; Black hemp

192 D
Teacher Time and Classic Alphabet sets; Garden Green, More Mustard, and Confetti Cream card stock; Basic Black, Going Gray, and Garden Green Classic pads; watercolor brush; 1/16" Circle punch; crochet thread

193 A
Fun Faces, Alphabet Fun Upper, Alphabet Fun Lower, and Mini Mates sets; Garden Green, Ruby Red, Close to Cocoa, and Ultrasmooth Vanilla card stock; Ruby Red and Basic Black Classic pads; watercolor brush; Black and Creamy Caramel eyelets; Nature template; 1/16" Circle punch; crochet thread

193 B
Fun Faces and Simple Sayings II sets; Ruby Red, More Mustard, Ultrasmooth Vanilla, and Garden Green card stock; Ruby Red, Garden Green, and More Mustard Classic pads; watercolor brush; Stampin' Dimensionals; 1/16" Circle punch; Natural hemp; sewing machine and thread

193 C
I Love Music set; Makin' Music wheel; Garden Green, Ruby Red, Ultrasmooth Vanilla, Radiant White vellum, and More Mustard card stock; Ruby Red Classic pad; Basic Black cartridge; More Mustard eyelet; Black hemp; Stampin' Dimensionals; sewing machine and thread

193 D
I Love Music set; Ruby Red, Basic Black, and Confetti Cream card stock; Confetti Cream tag sheet; Basic Black, Going Gray, Ruby Red, Really Rust, and More Mustard Classic pads; watercolor brush; Black eyelet; Black hemp; 1/16" Circle punch; Stampin' Dimensionals

194 A
Year-Round Fun and Simple Sayings sets; Brilliant Blue, Real Red, and Ultrasmooth White card stock; Real Red and Brilliant Blue Classic pads; White Craft pad; VersaMark pad; Heat 'n Stick powder; Dazzling Diamonds glitter; Brilliant Blue eyelet; Blue hemp; 26-gauge Wire Works; Stampin' Dimensionals

194 B
Kids at Play and All-Year Cheer I sets; Summer Sun, Brilliant Blue, Confetti White, and Green Galore card stock; Basic Black, Green Galore, Summer Sun, Only Orange, Blush Blossom, Brilliant Blue, and Pretty in Pink Classic pads; watercolor brush; 1/8" Circle punch; Apple Green grosgrain ribbon

194 C
Kids at Play and Simple Sayings sets; Brilliant Blue, Confetti White, Summer Sun, and Real Red card stock; Basic Black, Real Red, Brilliant Blue, Blush Blossom, Summer Sun, Creamy Caramel, and Chocolate Chip Classic pads; watercolor brush; Brilliant Blue eyelets

195 A
Little Trucks and Bold Alphabet sets; Brilliant Blue, Real Red, Summer Sun, and Confetti White card stock; Basic Black, Summer Sun, Brilliant Blue, Going Gray, and Real Red Classic pads; Real Red Craft pad; VersaMark pad; journaling marker; watercolor brush; Silver eyelets; 22-gauge Wire Works; 1/8" Circle punch; washers

195 B
Monster Mania and All-Year Cheer II sets; Gable Green, Green Galore, Basic Black, Real Red, and Summer Sun card stock; VersaMark pad; Basic Black Classic pad; Black detail embossing powder; 1/16" Circle punch; watercolor brush; Black grosgrain ribbon; embroidery floss; bleach

196 A
Paper Dolls set; Basic Black, Sage Shadow, and Perfect Plum Classic pads; Garden Green, Sage Shadow, Eggplant Envy, Positively Pink, Blush Blossom, Summer Sun, Barely Banana, Chocolate Chip, Pretty in Pink, Perfect Plum, Close to Cocoa, and Brocade Blue markers

196 B
Paper Dolls and All-Around Alphabet sets; Barely Banana, Brocade Blue, Eggplant Envy, and Ultrasmooth White card stock; Eggplant Envy and Basic Black Craft pads; Creamy Caramel, Barely Banana, Brocade Blue, Blush Blossom, Summer Sun, Pretty in Pink, Eggplant Envy, Basic Black, and Bliss Blue markers; font CD

197 A
Paper Pals and Alphabet Fun Lower sets; Brocade Blue, Barely Banana, and Ultrasmooth White card stock; Ultrasmooth White Circle AlphaAccents; Brocade Blue and Summer Sun Craft pads; VersaMark pad; Blush Blossom, Summer Sun, More Mustard, and Basic Black markers; journaling marker; Stampin' Dimensionals; Bordering Blue eyelets

197 B
Paper Pals set; Basic Black Classic pad; Blush Blossom, Brocade Blue, Chocolate Chip, Real Red, Barely Banana, Bliss Blue, Basic Black, Garden Green, and Creamy Caramel markers

198 A
Scouts at Play set; Mellow Moss, Confetti White, and Confetti Tan card stock; Mellow Moss and Basic Black Classic pads; watercolor pencils; font CD

198 B
Scouts at Play set; Night of Navy, Bordering Blue, Rose Red, and Confetti White card stock; VersaMark pad; Stampin' Pastels; Brilliant Blue star eyelets; White grosgrain ribbon; font CD

198 C
Girl Power and Classic Alphabet sets; Confetti Tan, Confetti Cream, Mellow Moss, and Close to Cocoa card stock; Close to Cocoa, Mellow Moss, Creamy Caramel, Only Orange, Real Red, Really Rust, Positively Pink, Chocolate Chip, Blush Blossom, and Yoyo Yellow Classic pads; watercolor brush; Close to Cocoa square eyelets; Natural hemp; Creamy Caramel eyelets

199 A
Polar Express and Classic Alphabet sets; Bordering Blue, Creamy Caramel, and Confetti White card stock; Baroque Burgundy, Basic Black, Creamy Caramel, Brocade Blue, Bordering Blue, and Going Gray Classic pads; watercolor brush

199 B
Dance Sketches and Classic Alphabet sets; Baroque Burgundy and Confetti Tan card stock; Victorian Designer Series vellum; Baroque Burgundy and Chocolate Chip Craft pads; journaling marker; stamping sponge; Burgundy wide organdy ribbon; buttons

200 A
Puck Play set; Ruby Red, Basic Black, Mellow Moss, Creamy Caramel, and Confetti Cream card stock; Basic Black, Mellow Moss, Garden Green, Creamy Caramel, Ruby Red, and Blush Blossom Classic pads; watercolor brush; paper crimper; Black eyelets; Natural hemp; Stampin' Dimensionals

200 B
Puck Play set; Ruby Red, Creamy Caramel, Ultrasmooth Vanilla, and Basic Black card stock; Basic Black and Ruby Red Classic pads; Stampin' Dimensionals

200 C
On the Green and Birthday Greetings sets; Stipple Plaid background stamp; Garden Green, Mellow Moss, Ruby Red, Confetti Cream, and Ultrasmooth Vanilla card stock; Basic Black, Ruby Red, Garden Green, Blush Blossom, Chocolate Chip, and Brocade Blue Classic pads; watercolor brush

201 A
Take Me Out to the Ballgame and Classic Alphabet sets; Creamy Caramel, Mellow Moss, Basic Black, Radiant White vellum, and Ruby Red card stock; Basic Black craft pad; Creamy Caramel eyelets; font CD; crochet thread; needle

201 B
Rough & Tumble and All-Year Cheer I sets; Garden Green, Mellow Moss, Ultrasmooth Vanilla, Basic Black, and Radiant White vellum card stock; Basic Black, Real Red, Garden Green, Bliss Blue, Blush Blossom, Chocolate Chip, and Mellow Moss Classic pads; Basic Black Craft pad; watercolor brush

204 A
Party Fun wheel; Green Galore, Ultrasmooth White, and Brilliant Blue card stock; Green Galore cartridge; paper crimper; Stampin' Dimensionals; Blue hemp; Green Galore eyelets

213 A
All-Year Cheer II and On the Line sets; Ultrasmooth White and Pretty in Pink card stock; Candy Designer Series vellum; Rose Romance Classic pad; Stampin' Dimensionals; 26-gauge Wire Works; Silver eyelets

214 A
Let's Party set; Subtles solid color paper; Sage Shadow and Lavender Lace Classic pads; Sage Shadow eyelets; Envelope Template Assortment I

215 A
Snowy Play and Simple Sayings II sets; Not Quiet Navy and Confetti White card stock; Basic Black, Bliss Blue, Only Orange, Not Quite Navy, Chocolate Chip, and Creamy Caramel Classic pads; Small Plaidmaker; sponge brayer; Creamy Caramel eyelets; watercolor brush; Natural hemp

216 A
Toile Blossoms set; Ballet Blue Craft pad; Ivory wide organdy ribbon; large portrait frame

216 B
Toile Blossoms set; Mellow Moss Craft pad; portrait accordion frame

216 C
Sparkling Season, Quirky Alphabet Upper, and Quirky Alphabet Lower sets; Candycane Craze wheel; Real Red, Confetti White, and Glorious Green card stock; Confetti White 8-1/2" x 11" Days-to-Remember Calendar; Basic Black and Real Red Craft pads; Real Red cartridge; Stampin' Dimensionals; Real Red star eyelets; Font CD

216 D
Happy Hearts set; Real Red and Ultrasmooth White card stock; Confetti White birthday calendar; Real Red, Mauve Mist, and Lavender Lace Classic pads; journaling marker; Real Red eyelets; 1/8" Circle punch

216 E
Little Shapes and Classic Alphabet sets; Rose Romance, Ballet Blue, Yoyo Yellow, Basic Black, and Green Galore Classic pads; rectangle sticker

216 F
Love without End set; Lavender Lace card stock; Ultrasmooth White tag; stampable memo cube; Lavender Lace, Mellow Moss, Orchid Opulence, and Lovely Lilac Classic pads; 1/8" Circle punch; Spring Moss grosgrain ribbon

216 G
By Design set; Real Red and Brocade Blue card stock; Basic Black and Night of Navy Classic pads; vinyl checkbook covers

216 H
Paper Dolls and All-Year Cheer II sets; Rose Romance, Confetti White, and Barely Banana card stock; Rose Romance, Barely Banana, Close to Cocoa, Creamy Caramel, and Basic Black Classic pads; Rose Romance marker; Clear colored envelope

217 A
Nice & Narrow set; Forest Foliage, Glorious Green, and Real Red card stock; Forest Foliage and White Craft pads; Brights Fabrico markers; White PolyShrink; 1/8" Circle punch; Natural hemp; Stampin' Dimensionals

217 B
Tags & More and Classic Alphabet sets; Gold Sculpey; 1/8" Circle punch; Orchid narrow organdy ribbon; Misty Lavender and Spring Green Pearl Ex; watercolor brush

217 C
Fall Whimsy set; Close to Cocoa, Chocolate Chip, and Creamy Caramel card stock; Paperclay; Chocolate Chip Classic pad; Natural hemp

217 D
Holiday Hedgehogs set; Checkerboard background stamp; Kraft card stock; Baroque Burgundy, Close to Cocoa, and Basic Black Classic pads; watercolor brush; Red hemp; Stamp-A-Mug

217 E
Crayon Cuties and Crayon Fun Alphabet Upper sets; Garden Green, Forest Foliage, and Real Red Classic pads; puzzle

218 A
Sweet Treats, Fun Phrases, All-Year Cheer II, Mini Mates, and Merry Elves sets; Radiant White vellum, Confetti Cream, and Pretty in Pink card stock; Real Red, Ultrasmooth White, Ultrasmooth Vanilla, Pretty in Pink, and Ballet Blue tag sheets; Basic Black, Real Red, Mellow Moss, Gable Green, Barely Banana, Pretty in Pink, Blush Blossom, Mauve Mist, and Brocade Blue Classic pads; VersaMark pad; watercolor brush; Heat 'n Stick powder; Dazzling Diamonds Glitter; 26- and 22-gauge Wire Works; Neutrals and Subtles fibers; Pretty in Pink, Silver, and Mellow Moss eyelets; Stampin' Dimensionals

218 B
Nice & Narrow set; Mellow Moss, Pale Plum, and Ultrasmooth White card stock; large bookmark; Basic Black, Mellow Moss, Perfect Plum, and Pale Plum Classic pads; Spring Moss grosgrain ribbon; paper crimper

218 C
All God's Children set; Soft Swirls background stamp; Confetti White, Orchid Opulence, and Summer Sun card stock; mini bookmark; Basic Black, Summer Sun, Really Rust, Orchid Opulence, Blush Blossom, and Gable Green Classic pads; watercolor brush; Folk Heart punch; Brights fiber

218 D
Jolly Old Elf and Background Basics sets; Confetti White card stock; Confetti White circle gift tag; Basic Black, Real Red, Not Quite Navy, More Mustard, Garden Green, Bordering Blue, Blush Blossom, and Mauve Mist Classic pads; Basic Black marker; watercolor brush; Stampin' Dimensionals; Real Red large circle eyelet; Neutrals fiber

218 E
Sparkling Season and All-Year Cheer II sets; Groovy Lines background stamp; Ultrasmooth White and Glorious Green card stock; Ultrasmooth White door hanger pouch; Real Red Classic pad; 22-gauge Wire Works

218 F
Jolly Old Elf set; Holiday Print background stamp; Bordering Blue, Basic Black, and Baroque Burgundy card stock; Baroque Burgundy Classic pad; Jet Black StazOn pad; Brights, Earths/Regals, and Pastels Fabrico markers; large oval porcelain ornament; Stampin' Dimensionals; French Blue grosgrain ribbon; Silver Mini Deco Fasteners

219 A
Enchanted Snowflakes and All-Year Cheer II sets; Confetti White card stock; Night of Navy party favor box; Night of Navy Classic pad; White Craft pad; Basic Black marker; Night of Navy eyelet; 1/16" Circle punch; Silver metallic cord

219 B
Sparkling Season set; Candycane Craze wheel; Real Red pouch box and tag; Gold metallic pad and refill; Basic Black cartridge; Gold Glory embossing powder; watercolor brush; Gold metallic ribbon

219 C
Simply Sweet and Simple Sayings I sets; By Definition background stamp; Old Olive, Confetti Cream, and More Mustard card stock; More Mustard and Old Olive stationery boxes; Basic Black, More Mustard, Old Olive, Ruby Red, and Not Quite Navy Classic pads; watercolor brush; Stampin' Dimensionals; crochet thread; needle

219 D
Dino-Mite set; Summer Sun, Garden Green, and Confetti White card stock; Old Olive trapezoid box; Old Olive and Garden Green Classic pads; watercolor brush; Stampin' Dimensionals; Gold hemp

220 A
Let's Party set; Groovy Lines background stamp; Ultrasmooth White and Real Red card stock; Ultrasmooth White tag; large white gable box; Real Red Classic pad; Red wide organdy ribbon; White and Real Red eyelets; crochet thread

220 B
Holiday Basics set; Night of Navy, Real Red, and Glorious Green card stock; white gift sack; White Craft pad; Silver star eyelets

220 C
Holiday Basics and All-Year Cheer I sets; Glorious Green, Ultrasmooth White, and Real Red card stock; white lunch bag; Real Red and Glorious Green Classic pads; 1/8" Circle punch; Silver star eyelets; Stampin' Dimensionals

220 D
Stars & Swirls set; Kraft card stock; small and medium kraft gift boxes; Night of Navy and Real Red Craft pads; Dazzling Diamonds glitter; Heat 'n Stick powder; Red grosgrain ribbon; Stampin' Dimensionals

220 E
Choo Choo and Classic Alphabet sets; Just Jeans background stamp; Real Red and Kraft card stock; medium kraft gable box; Brilliant Blue, Yoyo Yellow, Real Red, Basic Black, and Glorious Green Craft pads; Brilliant Blue eyelet; Red grosgrain ribbon

220 F
Swirls & Blossoms background stamp; Jet Black StazOn pad; small organdy bag

223 A
Crazy Alphabet and By Design sets; Naturals White, More Mustard, Old Olive, and Not Quite Navy card stock; Old Olive, Not Quite Navy, and More Mustard Classic pads; Jumbo circle punch; Old Olive oval eyelet; French Blue grosgrain ribbon

224 A
Fishy Friends set; Bliss Blue, Not Quite Navy, and Brocade Blue card stock; VersaMark pad; 22-gauge Wire Works; Stampin' Dimensionals

225 A
All God's Children set; Swirls & Blossoms background stamp Tempting Turquoise, Green Galore, Lovely Lilac, and Confetti White card stock; Basic Black and Tempting Turquoise Classic pads; watercolor pencils; watercolor brush; Tempting Turquoise triangle eyelets

226 A
Little Shapes set; Mellow Moss and Ultrasmooth White card stock; Bliss Blue, Mellow Moss, and Perfect Plum Classic pads

226 B
All-Year Cheer I and Fall Fun sets; Kraft and Not Quite Navy card stock; Close to Cocoa and Chocolate Chip Classic pads; paper crimper; Creamy Caramel eyelets; Natural hemp

229 A
Green Galore, Positively Pink, and Lavender Lace card stock; Love without End brass template; Positively Pink, Green Galore, Lovely Lilac, and Only Orange eyelets; Light Orchid grosgrain ribbon; Corner rounders

230 B
Mini Medleys and Fun Phrases sets; Basic Black and Brushed Gold card stock; VersaMark pad; Interference Gold, Interference Blue, and Interference Red Pearl Ex; stipple brushes; Stampin' Dimensionals; 26-gauge Wire Works

230 A
Stipple Shells and Vogue Verses sets; Creamy Caramel and Not Quite Navy card stock; Basic Black Classic pad; VersaMark pad; Spring Green, Super Russet, Misty Lavender, and Turquoise Pearl Ex; stipple brushes

231 A
Cheery Chat set; Swirls background stamp; Cameo Coral and Barely Banana card stock; Cameo Coral Classic pad; VersaMark pad; Dazzling Diamonds glitter; Heat 'n Stick powder; White large circle eyelets; White grosgrain ribbon; Stampin' Dimensionals; Folk Heart punch

232 A
Autumn and All-Year Cheer II sets; Eggplant Envy, Lovely Lilac, and Confetti Cream card stock; Eggplant Envy Classic pad; skeleton leaves; Ivory wide organdy ribbon; Stampin' Dimensionals

232 B
Crazy for Christmas set; Swirls background stamp; Real Red, Glorious Green, and Confetti White card stock; Basic Black, Going Gray, Real Red, Glorious Green, and Yoyo Yellow Classic pads; Stampin' Dimensionals; Cranberry grosgrain ribbon; Gold Mini Deco Fasteners

232 C
By Design and Simple Sayings II sets; Summer Sun, Ultrasmooth White, and Real Red card stock; Real Red and Basic Black Classic pads; 22- and 26-gauge Wire Works; needle

232 D
Nice & Narrow set; Radiant White vellum, Bliss Blue, Ultrasmooth White, and Gable Green card stock; Brocade Blue and Gable Green Classic pads; White Craft pad; Font CD; Silver Mini Deco Fasteners

233 A
Cute as a Bug set; Real Red, Basic Black, and Confetti White card stock; Basic Black Classic pad; Real Red heart eyelet

233 B
Nice & Narrow and All-Year Cheer I sets; Green Galore, Real Red, Radiant White vellum, and Confetti White card stock; Real Red and Green Galore Classic pads; Stampin' Pastels; VersaMark pad; Ruby Red square eyelets

233 C
Classic Alphabet set; Confetti White, Night of Navy, and Real Red card stock; Silver star eyelets

233 D
All-Year Cheer III set; Real Red, Green Galore, and Confetti White card stock; Confetti White tag; Real Red Classic pad; Daisy punch; White small flower eyelet; Yoyo Yellow large flower eyelet; Stampin' Dimensionals; 22-gauge Wire Works

Proprietary Rights in Trademarks and Copyrights

The contents of this catalog are protected by federal trademark and copyright registrations. Reproduction of the catalog or any portion thereof is strictly prohibited.

Purchasers of Stampin' Up!® products are authorized to sell hand-stamped artwork made with our copyrighted designs only in accordance with Stampin' Up!'s angel policy, a copy of which can be found on the Stampin' Up!® Web site at www.stampinup.com, or obtained from a Stampin' Up!® demonstrator. Permission is not granted to mechanically reproduce stamped images.

Ordering

All products in this catalog may be purchased only through a Stampin' Up!® demonstrator. Demonstrators are independent contractors and are not employees of Stampin' Up!® To help your demonstrator ensure accuracy in taking your order, always include item number, description, and price of each item ordered. Your demonstrator will provide you with two copies of your order. Please retain these copies for your personal records. You have a right to cancel order within 3 days (US; 10 days in Canada) of placing it. Ask your demonstrator for more details.

Delivery

We ship through the best carrier available. Product is usually shipped to deliver within seven business days from the date the order is received by the company. (not applicable in Canada) Stampin' Up!® shall not be liable for any delay in shipment that is caused in whole or in part by circumstances beyond Stampin' Up!®'s control.

Guarantee

We guarantee products to be free from manufacturing defects for a period of 90 days after the shipping date. Missing items, incorrect shipments, and defective or damaged merchandise must be reported to your demonstrator within 90 days of the shipping date. This guarantee does not cover merchandise damaged through accident or misuse. If you should require assistance, please contact your demonstrator.

Exchanges & Refunds

New, unused merchandise may be exchanged at no charge within 90 days of the shipping date. The merchandise must be in the current catalog and in original shipping condition. Stamps that have been assembled cannot be exchanged. Sorry, we do not offer cash refunds. The customer is responsible for return shipping charges. If you should require assistance, please contact your demonstrator.

Limitations

Stampin' Up!® reserves the right to issue a refund or substitute merchandise of similar quality and value for items that are discontinued or out of stock. The decision to discontinue merchandise and the choice of whether to issue a refund or substitution belongs solely to Stampin' Up!® The items sold are craft items, and your results may vary from the examples shown. Also, actual stamps may vary somewhat in size from the images shown in this catalog, and this difference in size shall not be deemed a manufacturing defect.

Information about properties of certain products (such as acid content, lignin content, and other properties affecting a product's performance or suitability for a particular use) is supplied by the product manufacturers and/or suppliers. Stampin' Up!® relies on this information and does not conduct independent tests to verify the accuracy of the information supplied by product manufacturers and suppliers.

Trademark Ownership

3L is a registered trademark of 3L Corporation. MetaleXtra is a trademark and Top Boss is a registered trademark of Clearsnap, Inc. Paperclay is a registered trademark of Creative Paperclay Co., Inc. Empressor, Painty, and Stamp-a-ma-jig are trademarks and Zig is a registered trademark of EK Success. Hermafix is a registered trademark of HERMA GmbH + Co KG. Lumiere is a registered trademark of Jacquard products manufactured by Rupert Gibbon & Spider Inc. Cropper Hopper is a trademark of Leeco Industries. PolyShrink is a trademark of Lucky Squirrel. Inkworx is a registered trademark of P&M Promotions, Ltd. Plaidmaker is a trademark of Stampin' Up!, Inc. AlphaBuilders, Bold Brights, Color Coach, Classy Brass, Definitely Decorative, Earth Elements, Embossing Buddy, On Stage, Rich Regals, Soft Subtles, Stampin' Around, Stampin' Dimensionals, Stampin' Emboss, Stampin' Flock, Stampin' Glitter, Stampin' Ink, Stampin' Kids, Stampin' Memories, Stampin' Mist, Stampin' Pads, Stampin' Pastels, Stampin' Scrub, Stampin' Spot, Stampin' Up! and the boxed logo of the words Stampin' Up!, Stampin' Write, and Two-Step Stampin' are registered trademarks of Stampin' Up!, Inc. Permanent Mono is a registered trademark of American Tombow Inc. StazOn and VersaMarker are trademarks and Encore!, Kaleidacolor, and VersaMark are registered trademarks of Tsukineko. Liquid Applique is a trademark of Uchida of America Corporation. Mini Deco Fasteners is a trademark of American Pin. Premo Sculpey is a trademark of Polyform Products Co. Inc.

Stampin' Up!®
9350 South 150 East, Fifth Floor
Sandy, Utah 84070

www.stampinup.com

Join
the Stampin' Up! *family*

Do you love stamping and being creative?

Thousands of women and men throughout the United States and Canada have turned their love for stamping into a way to earn extra money, enjoy a discount on Stampin' Up! products, or start a fun new career. You'll experience this when you become a Stampin' Up! demonstrator! Join the growing family of Stampin' Up! demonstrators who are able to share their love of stamping while having the convenience of setting their own schedules. You can, too, with complete training and support from an established leader in the stamping and scrapbooking industry.

Our starter kit contains everything you need to begin— training videos, product guide, catalogs, order forms, and (of course!) rubber stamps and accessories. And you can quickly add to your collection of sets with our Stampin' Start program, designed to reward you for successfully starting your Stampin' Up! business. In addition, Stampin' Up! demonstrators enjoy spending time with old and new friends at annual conventions, as well as other training and recognition events.

Want to get started?

Call your demonstrator or Stampin' Up! today to learn more! You'll be glad to be a part of the fun and warmth of Stampin' Up!

1-800-STAMP UP
www.stampinup.com